REAPPEAR

THOUGHTS OF LEAVING
BOOK II
REAPPEAR

TESS HAMILTON

BALANCE

Published by Perfect Balance Publishing

REAPPEAR: Thoughts of Leaving Book II

Based on a true story

Copyright © 2021 Tess Hamilton

Cover Copyright © 2021 Tess Hamilton

Cover Design by Tara Mayberry at TeaberryCreative.com

Editing and Formatting by Stacey Smekofske at EditsByStacey.com

BALANCE
PERFECT
PUBLISHING

Identifiers:

Hardcover 978-1-7348597-3-7

Paperback 978-1-7348597-4-4

E-Book 978-1-7348597-5-1

In memory of my dear friend and comrade, Captain James Maxwell Douglass.

The bond that links your true family is not one of blood, but of respect and joy in each other's life.

— RICHARD BACH

CONTENTS

FROM PACIFIC TO SIERRA

*J*ust down the road from my parent's home, the small town of Jackson was peacefully nestled in the foothills of Northern California. It had a quaint main street lined with boutiques, bars and cafes. The streets resonated with energy from the 1800s, as though nothing had changed. The hitching posts that once fastened a miner's horse remained in the cobblestones along the narrow walkways. A sign hung above the law offices of Meager and Moore. I walked into the office and took a seat in the waiting area. "It was time," I told myself. It was time to file for a divorce.

SNOW HAD FALLEN OVERNIGHT. IT WAS MARCH 1979, AND MY KARMANN Ghia looked like just another mound of snow outside my parent's home. They had comfortably settled into their cabin in the woods. "Look, Tess. There must be three feet of new snow," my mother hollered as I prepared for another day at work.

Father and Mother succeeded in setting up a small business since moving to the mountains. I had taken employment in their accounting office, and it was just enough space to accommodate the three of us. I was still safely enclosed within the secure walls, learning the fine workings of the accounting world. I was far from the familiar airports, and I no longer had the rolling tides from the San Francisco Bay to gaze upon. They had been replaced with snow, Ponderosa pine trees, and the smell of magnificent, incensed cedars.

As we made our way out of the house, I grabbed the snow shovel and trudged toward my car. Father interrupted, "No Tess, we can all ride in my VW bus." It handled well in these conditions. We arranged ourselves nicely in the chill of Father's bus, and we made our way down the small road onto Highway 88. The office was about a half mile south, and we trekked inch by inch in the heavily fallen snow. The wiper blades rocked back and forth, and I was mesmerized by their synchronized motion. I fell back into thoughts of my past and shivered.

Father chattered, non-stop, about his clients. Mother listened with a kindness in her eyes. I peered out the passenger window. I recalled the whistles and the hustle and bustle in Sao Paulo, Brazil. The blast of horns as vehicles narrowed on rear bumpers echoed in my mind. The stench of diesel exhaust and the eyes of people on the streets still lingered in my memory. I glanced at the back of my father's head covered by his knit ski cap; he continued chattering. His smile and dimples lit up the cold as his breath visibly floated across the steering wheel and onto the windshield.

How is it I ended up here? I felt like such a failure living with my parents again. My mind was saturated. I wondered if Elio Lencioni was still with the older woman? *Does he think of me?* I could almost smell his skin next to mine. My fingers had gently followed his rising chest down to his navel. I had gazed into his eyes. My mind pushed him away, and I thought of my Andre from Brazil.

It would be summer in Brazil right about now. The thought of wearing a swimsuit warmed me. My legs shivered and my toes felt frozen. "I am sure I prefer the summers more," I said to myself. However, I was back home, and life was starting over one more time. "One more time," my dance instructor would say as she clapped her hands. One more time as my feet riffed in each time step, graduating in tempo. "One more time," my lips murmured.

～

"I WANT YOU, LET'S DO IT AGAIN," I GESTURED WITH THE RISE AND FALL OF my eyebrow. Elio's mature home was nestled against the rolling hills on the east side of the San Francisco Bay. Rain fell, and we arrived after a day of shopping. It was late afternoon, and the sun was setting. Soft music played as Elio built a fire in his fireplace.

I slowly undressed as he stopped to observe me. With a youthful hesitation, I stood in just my bra and bikini underwear. Elio lifted me up with one swift move and unwrapped my remaining under garments. His style was that of a well-oiled engine, waiting to take flight. He braced me against the living room wall. Our breath intensified.

His body swayed with the grace of Fred Astaire. His whisper in my ear and the smell of his cologne pulled me in close. My heart raced as my legs straddled tightly around his waist. His strong arms held me up as though we were floating.

～

MY CHEST SWELLED AND MY BREATH FOGGED UP THE WINDOW IN MY father's VW van. I placed my finger on the glass and painted a trail down, down to his navel.

We arrived at the office and my parents lit a fire in the small wood stove centered in the middle of the room. The wood crackled as I stood in deep stillness. Mother brewed a pot of coffee. I shivered and drew in closer to warm by the fire. I imagined each flame mimicking a mood lamp's slow-moving fluid. After a moment, I quietly seated myself at the small desk set up for me in the corner. *My own little corner,* I thought to myself.

I remembered *Cinderella* in Rodgers and Hammerstein's production. Then I quickly turned my thoughts to Mr. Bob Cratchit in Charles Dickens's *A Christmas Carol.* He too sat in his own little corner rubbing his hands together to warm them. I began running my fingers up and down the keyboard of the 10-key calculator. My hands were covered in knit gloves with only my fingertips exposed. One two three, four five six, seven eight nine...zero. One two three, four five six, seven eight nine...zero. I repeated this over and over in my head, and closed my eyes, with my middle finger resting on number five. My finger pressed against the small, raised dot, indicating my hand was centered in the correct position. My movements came easy. Just like someone who was blind, I learned to navigate without radar, without visual reference, and without the light of a burning ember.

ELIO AND I FELL TO THE FLOOR, EACH OF US LYING ON OUR BACKS SMILING from exhaustion. "Let's eat, Tess," he said with a smile. "Stay here and lay by the fire, I want to admire you...all of you."

"Ok," I whispered.

I observed him cooking. He was a great cook. I gazed upon the flames dancing in the fireplace. I tuned into the clanking of pots and pans and the faint whistle as he worked. I imagined seven dwarfs marching along the hot embers under Elio's fireplace grate. Arthur's tirade in the kitchen sizzled in my mind. The smile on my face faded and took a 180-degree turn.

"HEY, TESS," MOTHER SNAPPED HER FINGERS IN FRONT OF MY FACE. SHE had startled me from another visit to the *Twilight Zone*. "I found this ad in the newspaper and thought of you. Pan American Airlines is hiring international flight attendants. You would be perfect, Tess. Why don't you apply?"

I carefully reviewed the newspaper and read through the list of requirements. It stated the applicant must be at least five feet two inches tall, and their weight must not exceed their body mass index. I pondered, *Would my ability to speak Portuguese be enough to give me a leg up?* I smiled as I continued reading; the interviews were in San Francisco and I could easily make that happen.

I decided I would apply. The idea of being in flight and traveling gave me a sense of meaning again. I was excited at the prospect.

That night, after working into the darkness of the Ponderosa pines, I wrote my resume. My body tingled from head to toe. Thoughts of leaving rekindled beneath my breath. The embers glowed, and Elio's smoke danced with misty thoughts of travel. Travel far-far away from here. Far from the shadows. Far from the residue. Far away was a good thought.

Those eyes: they were brown. Wait a minute, I needed to focus on my resume. I continued writing and finally finished my masterpiece. I placed my resume in the crisp white envelope and sealed it. *I wonder if they will consider me,* I thought.

I settled into my parents' guest room and burrowed into bed. I admired the walls decorated with clown artwork. Mother fashioned hand-blown glass clowns on the dresser and had placed more on each nightstand next to the bed. I adored her old and new paintings on the walls.

She had painted one piece in particular some years ago. As I gazed at the clown, I noticed the eyes. They were brown with a mole under the left eye. "She is good," I reminisced.

I visualized his extended hand; I had placed my palm on his and followed as we made our way onto the dance floor. I admired his stature, and the way he carried himself. He tipped his hat with a smile, and we began our dance while music slowed to a gliding rhythm. His cowboy boots slid back and forth, and I was once again taken away with that gleam in his brown eyes.

As I peered longer and longer at the painting, my optic shades became heavier and heavier. I hummed Leon Russell's song, "Tight Rope." I soon drifted off into the slumberland of Snow Circus Mountain.

FISH'N

*I*t was fall 1980. The morning was crisp, and I was awakened by the deep voice of Taj Mahal singing *Fishin' Blues*. The sun had just risen, and I thought to myself, *It is so early!* My heavy eyelids slowly opened, and I admired the 14-foot ceiling of the 1800s home. I squinted while my eyes focused on the old wallpaper of soft pink and green. Flowers were clustered together in symmetric rows that resembled chandeliers. A ceiling fan with its 4-foot extended neck hung from the ceiling. The tall windows were draped in old cloth curtains, and the window shades were drawn with large tassels at their base. I admired the golden oak antique dresser with a beveled mirror that tilted ever so slightly. Old beer mugs, with vintage Japanese fishing floats rested upon them, lined the dresser top.

I snuggled into the goose feathered pillow and pulled the soft quilt up to my chest. The musical notes filled the air, and soon Alessandro appeared in the bedroom. "Tess, get up! We are going fishing today." The smile upon his face showed genuine excitement, and the gleam in his eyes warmed my heart.

"Yes," I replied, but I frowned at the thought of fishing. No one had ever taken me fishing, and this new simplistic boyfriend loved to fish.

Alessandro Caminetti and I met on a blind date. I played women's softball, and my energetic coach decided he had the perfect mate for me. I wondered how perfect this man was I was about to meet.

A child of Italian immigrants, Alessandro grew up in Sutter Creek, California and was a local in Amador County, The Golden West. He was the youngest of four children and was operating the family business. Alessandro was handsome and tall with dark brown hair and brown eyes. He fashioned a beard that he kept short and well groomed. I immediately noticed his eyebrow; yes, his eyebrow. The brows had grown together in the center of his temple. He reminded me of Bert from *Sesame Street*. He had an incredible smile, and his enthusiasm for life lit up any room he entered.

Alessandro and I snuggled into his 1971 Chevrolet C10 and headed out to a nearby fishing spot. It was beautiful as we traveled along the small streams that skirted around Highway 49 that was nestled at the base of the Sierra Nevada Mountains. We occasionally stopped so I could take photographs. The stillness of the early morning mist covered a local pond. There was an old red barn sitting just beyond it. The quiet was softly interrupted with the faint click of my 35mm Minolta camera. The movement of the shutter, as it opened and closed, projected an echo across the water. Alessandro pulled me in close as we drove away, resting his arm around my shoulders. He was happy, but I was not sure if I should accept this feeling. My thoughts continued to race in and out while images of Elio lingered in the background.

Arthur, my ex-husband, called less and less frequently, and I found freedom in the distance I had put between us. Our distance was filled with Alessandro, and all my hopelessness was replaced with hope.

"Tess, it's a big one!" Alessandro hollered from the river below. I had hunkered down on a blanket to read. I looked over and observed a true fisherman at work. He wrestled with his fishing line and pulled in a fine catch. His Ray-Ban sunglasses gave him a sexy look, and I found him more and more attractive. I tip-toed carefully down the rocky path to the rushing water and admired his Chinook salmon. The sweat on his brow sent small beads of salty perspiration down his neck. The hair on his chest peeked out from the top of his flannel shirt, and I embraced him. "Looks like I may have only one catch today," Alessandro whispered with a slight grin.

The Mokelumne River rushed by my feet. I made my way back, ever so carefully so as not to fall on the slippery rocks. Alessandro continued with his fishing, and I returned to my blanket and opened *Illusions* by Richard Bach. My best friend Lexie McLane had given me the book on my 19th birthday. She knew me so well. I bathed in its adventures. I missed her company along with her words of wisdom. Her Hollywood smile had once earned her the first runner-up award in our small town, by the bay beauty pageant.

I drifted in and out of thoughts. My world was changing colors, and I pondered my own illusions and what that may look like.

As I gazed out of my cockpit window, I taxied over to my hanger with gentle movements against my rudder controls. "Right rudder," I told myself. I let out a sigh with a slightest of smile pressed against my lips. "Stop running, Tess," I whispered as images swarmed my mind.

BREAKING ROADS

*S*pringtime soon arrived, and the Daffodils and Chinese Sacred Lilies were in full bloom. I admired the rolling hills of Amador County gently covered in yellow, orange and shades of green. I drove south on Highway 88 and continued to Highway 49. I maneuvered the slow turns and soon arrived in the tiny town of Drytown. There was a post office, a small motel, and a café adjacent to it. Alessandro's Chevrolet C10 was parked in front of the café. I slowly pulled in and parked right alongside him. His grin and his intense brown eyes stared at me. It was Sunday, May 11, 1980, and I had agreed to meet his entire family. We were invited to his sister's home just outside of Drytown.

Alessandro's sister, Francesca, was second to the youngest. She was tall with long light brown hair. Her eyes were green, just like her father, and she had a bubbly personality. Francesca and her husband, Morgan, purchased a ranch and settled into a *back-to-the-land* lifestyle. Alessandro opened the passenger door, and I slid across the bench seat, positioning myself center stage.

We headed down New Chicago Road, leaving my car at the café, and we traveled beside an old wooden fence. His black Chevrolet C10 cruised slowly over a hill, unveiling the entrance of an opened wooden gate. Just beyond the gate sat an old white Ford Pickup. I noticed numerous old dolls and a few doll heads hanging over the fence posts. A sign above the gate read, "Dead Doll Ranch." I envisioned someone intentionally hammering their limbs to the wooden posts, and then I visualized a gavel.

～

"ORDER IN THE COURT," THE AMADOR COUNTY JUDGE CALLED THE NEXT case. I rose and approached the bench with my attorney. Arthur was seated at the opposing table and we began our court proceedings. Honorable Judge O'Reilly raised an eyebrow as he listened to Arthur rant and rave.

My attorney, Mr. Moore, argued on my behalf. "Your Honor, my client left with nothing more than her personal items in her 1958 Karmann Ghia. The two shared no property, no children and no assets. My client is asking for a divorce, and a small reimbursement for community property that Mr. Arthur retained."

Arthur argued over this, that, and whatever, and finally the judge ordered, "Enough. Case dismissed; divorce has been granted." It was a victory on my part. Arthur was obviously angry when he rose with clenched fists. I was free from his suppression, and I exhaled with relief. It felt as though the door had closed as the last passenger boarded the plane.

Arthur faded, our friends faded, and life in the San Francisco Bay area faded. All except for Elio. He was still there, and I could not escape that mental custody. I knew I had to let go and escape, but I wasn't ready to.

As I exited the courthouse, I thanked my attorney and noticed Arthur speeding away in his F150 pickup. The truck was a chocolate brown, and the tailgate had the name **FORD** spelled out in bold white lettering. "Ford," I whispered. *"For Our Repetitive Disaster,"* and then I smiled. The Ford grew smaller and smaller, and then the Ford slowly disappeared, just like the boys selling cigarettes on the streets in Bogota, Colombia.

ALESSANDRO'S HAND SHIFTED INTO A LOW GEAR AS WE TRAVELED UP THE dirt road to Dead Doll Ranch. Her small white 1800s home with green shutters was nuzzled between the rolling hills. I admired a massive 10-foot bay leaf tree planted at the end of her road. A garden displayed rows of tomatoes, swiss chard, wax peppers, and a variety of herbs. Her husband, Morgan, was attending to his BBQ sizzling with chicken. He waved to us as we slowed to a stop. "Nice truck!" I hollered at Morgan. "That's my white bird with a dirty tail!" he hollered back, grinning.

"Why Dead Doll Ranch?" I asked Alessandro. "My sister and her husband made the discovery while digging up the soil for their garden. They uncovered so many old dolls, they hung them on their entrance," he said with a wink.

"Creepy," I responded.

It gave me goosebumps, but then I switched gears and remembered the Church of Nosso Senhor do Bonfim in Salvador, Brazil. Their room of intentions held plastic limbs dangling from the ceiling, in recognition of the power of prayer. I smiled, and then I glanced back at Morgan; Morgan resembled Willie Nelson and my thoughts turned to Willie's hit song, "On the Road Again."

LANGUAGE FAILURES

I made my way down the busy Highway 88. Summer had ended, and I had finally received a response from Pan American Airlines. It was early August 1979 when I was scheduled for an interview at San Francisco International Airport. Mother was beside herself when I packed my bags and left for the Bay Area, making my first stop at Macys' department store in San Leandro. I selected a light brown wool skirt with a matching wool vest. I added a crisp white shirt along with a pair of leather pumps. I wanted to present myself professionally the next day. My sister Angie, still residing in San Leandro, offered a bed for the night, and along with her hair expertise, I took her up on the offer.

I arrived at her home and slowed my Karmann Ghia to a stop. My tires rested upon the same curb my father's car had on the day my brother passed away. I looked at the duplex my father had built and took comfort knowing another family lived in my previous residence at the rear. Arthur was finally gone, and yet I found myself a bit shaky looking at my childhood neighborhood where I lived with him. Darkness had cast a negative light, and a shadow of that still remained.

Angie was delighted at my reemergence. She and her husband, Mel, spent hours talking with me, catching up on our lives. She encouraged my chosen path and helped to ensure my appearance was in line with an interview of this magnitude.

The next morning, I was on my way to San Francisco Airport repeating words in Portuguese and hoping my foreign language skills would be good enough for hire. The drive over the San Mateo Bridge brought light into my life and with it hope. I rolled down my window and took in the salty air along with the sounds of seagulls above. "Home," I whispered. I breathed easy, that is, until a car went speeding by. Then more cars, one by one, sped past me, and there I was in the middle of traffic. I was quickly reminded of life in the city, and I had become comfortable living in the foothills.

Pan American Airlines was easy to find. As I pulled off the freeway at the airport exit, signs directed me to the large building next to the runways. The bold blue letters above the administrative offices guided me onward. I swung my car around and backed into the front parking space. I glanced in the rear-view mirror and applied some lip stick. It was stall or soar, and my knees began to shake.

As I entered the building, a young woman asked for my name. She checked that my name was on the list and eyed me up and down. "We had better weigh you and check your height," she prompted with a smile. She escorted me into a small room. I stood on a physician mechanical beam scale; she moved the lower bar to 50 pounds and then the upper bar, stopping at 49 pounds. My total weight was noted at 99 pounds. She then adjusted the height inner rod for my height; "Five foot two inches," she whispered. "Just the right height." She seemed very pleased. I was escorted into a room with eight other applicants. I was delighted when she gave me a small carryon blue bag. "Pan American Airlines," was printed on it. I took a seat and waited for further instructions.

"Hello everyone!" a stern-looking woman announced as she entered the room. I stood until instructed to be seated. She took roll call and proceeded to pass out papers for each of us based on the language we had indicated on our applications. I glanced over mine and noticed about ten sentences in Portuguese. I immediately felt flush. The nerves intensified from my toes moving to the top of my head. It was a test, and

I loathe tests. I was not that literate in the language, and I had no idea the meaning of the sentences. I took quick breaths and felt my mouth go dry.

Each applicant was asked to read the first three sentences and then translate their meaning. The facilitator began on the opposite side of the room, allowing me time to decipher my list. While waiting for my turn, I eyed the exits and resigned to the attempt. When her eyes rested on me, she asked that I read the *last* three sentences from the bottom up and interpret. I had figured out lines one through five, but I knew in that moment I was screwed. My eyes filled up with tears, and I stumbled over the words. I struggled with their meaning, and it became obvious to everyone in the room my Portuguese was terrible. The words seemed unfamiliar, and until that moment, it had not occurred to me how much the Brazilian dialect differed from Portugal.

"Wait, wait!" I wanted to scream out. "I can do this. I can speak Portuguese!" But my words danced across early morning clouds. I sat unnaturally still, embarrassed. My stature shrank with each second that passed. I withdrew and shriveled up, just like the Chinese Sacred Lily and the Daffodils on the rolling hills of Amador County.

I was excused from the interview shortly thereafter. I walked away feeling deflated. I should have explained myself, but I should have known better. My mother's confidence in me was much greater than my own. I started up my Karmann Ghia, using the push method and popping the clutch. I drove to the freeway and over the San Mateo Bridge. I surrendered. I was tired of chasing after something, someone, a dream, or a promise. I looked up at the jet passing overhead and fondly remembered my return from Colombia. I exited the Nimitz Freeway in Hayward and headed toward Elio's home. I needed my inner engine to be ignited.

I drove up the familiar curvy paved roads into the Hayward hills. The temperature was cool, and a slight breeze brushed against my hair. My senses instinctively shifted the four-speed transmission, and within seconds, I arrived in front of his house. Memories flooded in as I examined his black Porsche parked in the driveway. My nerves feathered from the botched-up interview. I needed his comfort and reassurance, but most of all I needed strength. I walked slowly to his entrance and rang the doorbell. It was quiet, and I almost turned and ran, but the door opened. It was him. Elio smiled. My knees buckled, and I wanted to crumple into his arms; so, I did.

My eyes welled up. A deafening ringing resonated within my ears, while my mind fixated on him. Elio carried me into his home, and with his gentle touch he closed the front door.

OBSTACLES

*I*t began as a bright and hopeful day, but then the sun found comfort behind the clouds surrounding the San Francisco Bay. Cool damp air settled against the cold sidewalks that lined the streets in Hayward, California. The afternoon sun slumped its eye lids as the evening sky overshadowed any hope for sunshine. I gazed out the bedroom window as Elio's breath brushed in and out against my cheek. My thoughts marched forward and backward, reminding me of *Babes in Toyland* from the 1934 Laurel and Hardy Christmas musical. I smiled at the thought of spending my life with Elio. I snuggled closer and remained still. I never wanted this moment to end. Elio had carried me into his home just like Tom-Tom did with Little Bo Peep. The music of Gordon Lightfoot's "If you could read my mind" played softly on the small radio next to his bedside. My smile then rescinded and my heart felt heavy. I wondered if Elio felt this way.

I drifted off, later awaking to the familiar sounds of pots and pans in the kitchen. For a brief second, I thought of Arthur in his drunken-drug induced tirades. I looked about the room in a sleepy state of confusion, relaxing when I remembered where I was. Elio had taken charge of cooking dinner for us. I slipped into his crisp shirt, which hung neatly across a chair under the window. I lightly danced into the kitchen and wrapped my arms around his waist. There it was... my vision against my fingertips.

Elio spun me around, lifting me onto his kitchen counter. "What's cooking?" I asked.

Elio covered my mouth and whispered, "A surprise! I just put our dinner into the oven, and it will bake about 45 minutes, so...let's take a shower." Elio swung me across his shoulder, patting my rear-end, and carried me to his shower.

Hot water ran over both our bodies as I gently lathered his back. My arms seemed so small against his tone of golden-brown skin. I looked up to him in every way, yet my insecurity remained locked inside my heart. Elio turned me around and raised me against him. His rhythm was slow and sensual. He cradled me as our passion became more and more intense until he no longer could hold me up. I turned and leaned against the shower wall, my back to him. My hands pressed against the glass and Elio's controlled, impetuous motions exploded. He held me tightly and whispered, "Nice ass."

Moments before arriving at Elio's home, I had been determined to reveal my genuine feelings to him. As we retired for dinner, my uncertainty was clearer. I sat my nice ass down on the kitchen chair and enjoyed a baked lasagna, salad, fresh sourdough bread (from Lucca's Italian Delicatessen), and fine wine. Elio spoke with enthusiasm and seemed genuinely happy to see me again. I listened intently and savored the moment.

"Stay the night, Tess. My friend Rick, called while you were sleeping. We are invited to join him and Kathy on the California Delta River tomorrow. He just bought a new ski boat. It will be fun, and I would love your company?" Elio asked with eagerness. I remembered my overnight suitcase was at my sister Angie's home.

"Ok, I can stay, but I need to run over to Angie's and get my bag." The lines around his eyes creased as he smiled. It was amusing to me when I realized I had packed my Brazilian Tanga swimsuit. I knew he would like it because my ass would be showing. I must have had a sixth sense.

At early dawn, Elio leaned over and drew me in. He wanted me and with little effort, his body cradled mine. I would have stayed forever, if only he had asked. I realized loving him was cavernous; what I did not know was how he felt about me. Elio never said the words, and a part of me withdrew, again. Maybe I was just a good piece of ass? I moved carefully, following his lead in our slow dance. He had control of my insecurity and somehow that did not settle with me.

The highway to the Delta was on my way home, so Elio and I opted to follow Rick and Kathy to the delta in my Karmann Ghia. I wanted to drive home after a day on the river and recount my steps.

We all boarded the ski boat and cruised in the warm sun. Kathy was a great water skier; she expertly swayed back and forth across the still estuary. There were moments when I sat on Elio's lap as he navigated the boat. Jackson Brown's "Stay Just a Little Bit Longer" blasted from the stereo system. My grin was beyond my control as we sped through the water; wind rushed through our hair as the bow of the boat slapped up and down against the water.

We stopped at an inlet with an outdoor bar, and we all disembarked for a drink. Rick quizzed me about my life in Amador County. He seemed to be inquiring about other men in my life. My body tensed up and my eyes fixed on his. I was getting the impression he was asking on Elio's behalf. I never admitted I was dating anyone else, but when Elio returned with some drinks in hand, Rick announced, "Hey Elio, Tess has a younger man back at home! She can't wait to get back to him." I was in shock, and all eyes were on me. I denied the accusation, but doubt leaked out of Elio's eyes and a shadow of suspicion came into full view. I whispered in his ear, "What about Beverly?" Our eyes searched each other for reassurance; there was none.

I drove home late in the evening on my sun burned ass. I shifted back and forth on my brown leather bucket seat. My white shorts prevented my burned skin from sticking to the seat. I turned the radio dial until finding Fleetwood Mac's "Landside." I let the words soak in.

Elio's eyes seemed lost when I departed for home. Our age difference played heavily on him once more. I was no longer sure if pursuing him was my destiny. I pictured myself as a kite. I was frail, subject to the winds, jetting back and forth against the sky's horizon. He held the string as he maneuvered my colorful layers of fabric and my tail trailing behind. My inner strength weakened around him. The wind had died, and I fell fast and hard to the ground.

I fumbled, lighting my cigarette. I turned up the volume on my radio. Fleetwood Mac's "Songbird" played. I needed to glide through the disappointment that set in. I had tripped over my interview, and I had tripped over my leading edge. It wasn't long before I did what I knew best; I ran, again.

PLAY BALL

I had spent six months with my parents, working hard in the world of accounting. I became disenchanted with living in the Sierra Nevada Mountains at our family cabin. It was time for me to move on, and my brother Albert had purchased a home just down the road. While Albert commuted between Stockton and Hayward, his new purchase was vacant during the week. It was a perfect setup for me, and I could keep watch over it for him. Between work for Southern Pacific Railroad and his studies at Hayward State University, Albert about collapsed when he crashed at Mel and Angie's house in San Leandro.

I moved in before another heavy winter fell on us. It was a quaint two-bedroom bungalow tucked high above the canyon surrounding Mace Meadows Golf Course and Country Club. I remember feeling a new sense of independence. I saw very little of my brother.

Leaves fell with shadows of Elio as each of my remaining family members relocated to Amador County. Mel and Angie were the only ones who stayed in San Leandro. My oldest sister, Katie, landed a job with the Amador County Board of Supervisors. My sister, Jessica, was hired as the clerk of the court in the Civil Court system, and my oldest brother, Martin continued his employment with Albert at Southern Pacific.

Months had passed. Katie and Jessica were social in the small town of Jackson, and it was not long before I was introduced to people my own age. Katie and her husband, Ace, had separated, and Katie was dating a nice young man named Marco, who was another local to The Golden West. He was of Italian descent and knew just about everyone in the county. I soon found myself on a double date with Katie and Marco, and that was when I met William.

William was also a local and knew everyone in town. He was two years older than me, handsome, and of German descent. It was refreshing to date someone new. He seemed to bring out the smile in me, and before long we socialized with many of his friends. William lived with two other occupants in a condominium in Sutter Creek. One roommate named James had a girlfriend that I immediately connected with. Her name was Demi, and she had big brown eyes and long brown hair. Demi and I shared the same age and interests. Demi included me in social functions. We met up for parties, dinners followed with dancing, and it seemed I was meeting more and more people in town. She was bubbly, friendly, and I really needed a girlfriend.

There was a local Italian Restaurant name Vecchio's in Jackson. Live bands played on the weekends in the bar. I met the mayor of Jackson there, and I was told he had the "Midas Touch." He was also Italian, and it seemed most people in Jackson were. The mayor and I shared a dance as Demi looked on, smiling. William never seemed the least bit jealous, and he felt more like a friend, and a bad one at that. He had wandering eyes, and I wasn't swept away by him as I was with Elio. My aura had drifted; bobbing up and down atop the distant caps in the San Francisco Bay while my heart clung to the notion that one has when young and filled with misconceptions.

I was delusional when thinking William may have been *the one*. That quickly dissipated when I realized he reminded me, too much, of my high school boyfriend Derk (only not as tall and not as handsome). Once I was aware of the correlation, I was guarded.

Demi and James remained my friends, and when February 1980 rolled around, they invited me to try out for a local woman's softball team. James and Marco were coaching, and I sprang at the opportunity to play. I knew I was pretty good at catching and running, so I gave it a shot.

I arrived at the baseball diamond at the local park. My brother, Albert, loaned me his baseball glove. My coaches instructed the team to run two laps around the field and line up at the dug-out. I was relieved to get back into running and get active again. After batting practice, catching, and rotating positions, I was chosen for the short-stop position. James felt that was the best position due to my ability to catch a fast ball.

We started playing games in the evenings and on weekends. Demi and I played on the same team, and our friendship grew. Albert, Katie, and William would show up at the games to cheer me on. It seemed my life was taking on new meaning, and when I looked back at my life in the Bay Area, I gained strength to forge forward. I enjoyed my time with the team that became known as "The team that lost at the last minute." It seemed we were always losing our games, but not without a fight. For some reason, the opposing team would pull ahead in the last inning to a victory. I reminded myself how I was taught to lose with dignity, and so I did. "Dignity," I whispered to myself. I held tightly on to that thought, along with faded childhood remnants of D-Band at summer camp in the Santa Cruz mountains.

One particular practice day, I arrived at the baseball diamond, and James confronted me. "I have your future husband for you!" he said with a grin. I looked at him with the same look my big sister Katie would give me; the one with the raised upper right side of my lip.

Demi approached and stood by James and reiterated, "He is perfect for you, Tess! If you are interested, we can all go out for dinner, and you can meet him? We can go to Vecchio's. Oh, by the way, his name is Alessandro."

SONG BIRD

I reached to shut down my Cessna 152 engine and ran through my checklist. The day was cool and the sky clear. I secured my control wheel and pushed the airplane back into the hanger. My mind continued to wander around my decisions from the past. "Use your voice," I whispered to myself. I shook my head, "If only," I hushed, and then I pulled the hanger door closed.

THE DRIVE HOME FROM THE DELTA SEEMED LIKE THE LONGEST DRIVE OF my life. Elio and I had departed with such uncertainty. Beverly continued to be a powerful force in his life, and he was the powerful force in mine. I could justify our sixteen years between us. He was so much more than a number to me. As the outline of the sun setting over the distant hills faded in my rear-view mirror, I rewound those feelings of starting over one more time. The radio station played memories, "The Way We Were." My heart sank.

William awaited my arrival from the Bay Area. We had just met a few weeks prior, and I promised to stop by his condo when I returned from my interview with Pan American Airlines. I pulled up in front. I sat in my Karmann Ghia for a few minutes, contemplating my decisions. I was confused and recalled my sister Katie juggling between boyfriends. I had just left the arms of Elio, and a sense of shame settled down on me. William had no knowledge of Elio, and I certainly had no intention of divulging.

I glanced at his front door again, and then I recalled the front door that opened to a welcoming smile of Elio. I could not move. William was not Elio. With relief, I fired up my car and drove away. I wanted to run until I could fly. There it was. Rick was correct in his assessment. I did have a younger man in my life. But in my heart, I knew William was temporary, as I was temporary to Elio.

Feelings of exhaustion overloaded my body. My loyal Karmann Ghia and I continued our journey home from the Delta. As I entered my brother's house, the phone rang. William was checking on me. "How was the interview, Tess? Did you forget to stop by?" he asked.

My voice felt as if I had lost control, and my words stumbled over each other. "I failed the language, and I am pretty sure I failed the interview. I was too tired to stop by," I knowingly reserved my reason. I feared he may have seen me drive away from his front curb.

William was sanguine and tried to cheer me up. It was useless. "How about going to a party with me Saturday night in Jackson?" he said with enthusiasm. "Demi, James, Marco, and Katie are going, and we could lift your spirits?" he persisted.

"Ok, what time will you pick me up?" I asked.

"How about seven pm?" William paused, "Plan on staying over, Tess; that way we won't have to drive back up to your brother's," he added.

With misgivings in my heart and an inability to say no, I agreed to go.

Saturday arrived, and I spent the afternoon getting ready for my date. I packed my Pan American overnight bag. The afternoon sun rested upon the great Sierra Nevada Mountain range, and I stood watching the sun drop behind their majestic peaks. I hovered over my telephone, in hopes it would ring. Evening fell, and the mantel clock struck seven. A feeling of abandonment settled over me, and quiet sounds of city streets hovered in the background. Arthur and his cold shadow crept into my mind, and I knew. I knew in my heart that William was not coming. The clock continued to strike eight, nine, and then, ten. I gathered up my nice, sorry *ass*, and went to bed.

The phone rang, and I fought with all my strength to ignore it. I pulled the covers over my head and thought of Elio. I yearned for his touch and his soft, reassuring voice. I wept and wished with all my heart that I could hate him. William repulsed me, and I hated myself for opening up to anyone and everyone. Isolating feelings moved back into my mind. I blew liquid bubbles as the globule liquid substance formed. A very distinct don't touch me bubble reappeared around me.

The next morning, Katie called. William arrived at the party alone. Rejection had its way, and my self-esteem crumbled. "Fuck him," I hissed. I made myself a cup of coffee and shivered by the morning fire.

I picked up the local newspaper that was sitting on the coffee table, and noticed an article, "Dance studio opening soon." The studio was located just down the highway, and I slowly perked up. I raised one eyebrow and tapped on the side of my coffee mug.

GLIDING

*I*t was June 1980. I peered out of the 747s window seat with my eyes fixed on the water below. Katie and I were in-bound for Honolulu, Hawaii. We had purchased a "Pleasant Hawaiian Holiday" tour. We departed from Oakland, California, and made the long six-hour flight to Hawaii. It was my first trip to the islands, and both of us were looking forward to time away. Katie had gone through a very difficult divorce, and my divorce from Arthur was finally over. We both anxiously awaited our time on the beach, bathing in rest and relaxation.

I watched the breaks of water below as they took on the familiar rhythm of the San Francisco Bay. Thoughts about my new chapter in life beat against the shore. I pondered the idea of looking for a new job in the Jackson area and relocating. The atmosphere in town was much more inviting than the remote mountains up the highway.

I could not distinguish between the feeling of being undesirable and the knowledge of recognizing a bad guy when I met one. I was raised to believe that everyone was good until they proved otherwise. What was it with men? How can they be loving and kind, and then in a blink of an eye, cold and callous?

We neared Honolulu, and I watched as the flaps deployed and our captain made his sweeping left base to final approach onto runway 26R.

Exhilaration pulsated in my body and my longing desire to fly crept in. It was in my blood, and the memories of flying with Father seemed to always be drifting over the horizons of my brain. I watched as the airplane slowed and the wheels gently squeaked onto the long asphalt. The plane stopped just before the taxiway, and I imagined the conversations between the tower and the cockpit crew.

Hawaii was majestic with its sharp mountain peaks and lush green tropical foliage. Clouds lounged about Diamond Head Volcanic cone, and my eyes scanned the coastal edge. The island of Oahu was just what I needed.

Katie and I gathered outside the airport with the rest of our tour group. We were greeted by Island women who presented us with a Heliconia flower lei. The temperature was hot and Hawaiian music played from the terminal. The tropical flowers were pungent, making it difficult to hold back our smiles. We ignored our tour bus and opted to hail a cab. I watched as the bus departed with the numerous couples. Most were much older, and my sister and I did not want to hang with them. We grabbed our cab and headed to Paradise Hotel.

We approached the main desk in the lobby. I inquired about our reservation, and the clerk indicated we did not have one. Katie was instantly frustrated and informed him we were with the Pleasant Hawaiian Holiday group. He frowned and instructed us to proceed to the opposite end of the hotel lobby and check in there.

We slogged down the long hallway, and when we approached the end, I noticed the air conditioning had ceased and the carpet changed color. The check-in desk was small, and the décor was not as pleasant as the grand entrance we had left. Katie tapped the small bell resting upon the desk, and we waited for someone to help us.

It was not long before a bell captain arrived and escorted us to our room. We traveled the small elevator to the sixth floor. The room was small with two twin beds. My eyes scanned the contents of the room, and I asked the bell captain, "Where is our television?" He responded, "If you want a T.V., you will need to return to the front desk and request one." This seemed odd to me, but Katie and I returned to the lobby and inquired. We were told a black and white would cost ten dollars, and if we wanted color, it would cost twenty in cash. I was outraged. Katie and I really wanted one, so we paid the ten dollars for a black and white television. The front desk receptionist informed us to go to the third floor and knock on the housekeeping door. We could pick up our set. Katie and I grudgingly proceeded to the third floor. I knocked on the door, staring at "Housekeeping," embossed in white and waited. The door opened to a large man standing in front of numerous television sets stacked one on top of the other. We asked for our black and white. Katie and I had to carry it, rabbit ear style antenna and all, up to our room.

Our Pleasant Hawaiian Holiday tour was anything but pleasant. We were ignored by most of the hotel staff, but our rooms were supplied with fresh towels—at least. Each morning we awoke to street sounds and the arrival of a garbage truck. Our window overlooked the back of the hotel where the twenty-yard garbage dumpster sat. The beep-beep sound as the truck backed in was a reminder of our Cuckoo-clock back home.

Katie was on the phone every evening talking with Marco. She had fallen in love with this man. I battled with her about going out at night. She wanted to retire early and bathe in her melancholy distance from the mainland, which was transfixed on Marco. We soaked up the Hawaiian sun by the pool and occasionally walked around the grand city of Waikiki, taking in the large shopping mall and restaurants. The beaches were very crowded, and the only day we parked our nice *asses* on the beach, we were approached by a photographer.

He gave us his business card with a flyer and asked if we would come by his studio for some free photos.

The next day, we found the quaint little studio. It was settled in the heart of Honolulu among the surrounding high rises. A picture window displayed many photographs of beautiful women. When we entered, a small bell rang above the entry door. Mr. Photographer smiled as he greeted us. He escorted us to a back room and asked who would like to start? Katie went first and then me.

While I sat on a leather bench listening to his shutter lens snapping frame after frame, he paused and asked if I would be interested in posing nude? I was stunned. Naïve as I was and continued to be, this was nothing new. There I sat with my mouth hanging open in disbelief. "No thank you," was all I could say. It was like those seemingly never-ending mystery phone calls at my parents' home in San Leandro. I stood frozen, listening to his lurid propositions. The photographer came back into focus, and I quietly stood and walked away.

We left with our free photograph and headed back to Paradise Hotel. I asked Katie if the photographer asked her to pose nude. He did not. We chuckled, looking down at our 8x10 images. Katie was beautiful with her Hawaiian tan, long blonde hair, and lei around her neck. I looked like a poodle dog. I had recently cut my hair short, and the naturally curly hair shot out from my head in a round halo. I looked like I sported a blonde afro. With the tropical climate, it was nearly impossible for me to style my hair any other way. I looked down at my photo again and fought the urge to bark. The image took be back to one particular time with my high school classmate, Darcie.

POODLES

arcie and I seemed to find mischief whenever we hung out together. Alameda, California is a small island just a few miles, as a crow flies, from Oakland International Airport. Every Sunday, Alameda's Island Auto Movie Drive-In showcased a flea market or swap meet.

It was a warm day in the fall of 1973. I picked up Darcie in my 58 Karmann Ghia and headed to the flea market. We chatted about whatever was the talk of the town and listened to the radio as we cruised down Doolittle Drive toward Alameda. Darcie had a big smile on her face, and she always had a look in her eyes. It was a curious look, full of wonder and adventure. Music blasted in and out of our small talk, and I turned up the volume for Santana's "Evil Ways."

We arrived at the venue and pulled into a parking space that allowed me to position my car slightly downhill. I hesitated to switch off the radio. The music was perfect and made me want to dance. Santana's drums, lyrics, and guitar riffs added a lift to our mood.

We walked up and down the rows of vendors, stopping to admire their goods. I caught sight of Darcie eyeing a display of wigs. They were varieties of color and styles. I dashed over and we started trying on long shag-afro-style wigs. I selected the blonde one and Darcie chose black.

We loved the look and purchased them. I then found and bought a pair of John-Lennon-style eyeglasses from another vendor. The lenses were round and made of clear glass. When I put them on, it gave me a quintessential 70s look. We walked around the remaining rows of vendors wearing our wigs, and I was in my new eyeglasses, laughing every time we looked at each other.

The following Saturday night, we dressed up in our new wigs. I chose a pair of tie-dyed bell bottoms, a backless top that tied around the neck, platform shoes, and of course my new John-Lennon eyeglasses. It was the perfect disguise for an evening out in Oakland. Darcie and I drove to The Holiday Inn on Hegenberger Road. They had a live band on weekends, and we had our fake identification cards. It was going to be fun.

We entered the bar and were escorted to a bright orange leather booth, large enough for four people. We each ordered a screwdriver, since they were easy to sip. The music was too loud to talk, so we hung out watching the band. The room was dark, and the dance floor was small. The décor included low lighting to enable the stage for the band to be cast in slightly brighter lights. We did not recognize the group playing, but it was Motown music and an easy rhythm for dancing. It wasn't long before two older men approached us. They each scooted in alongside Darcie and me.

I felt like that white cougar from Brazil, looking into the brown eyes eager to converse with us. We exchanged a few smiles, danced a few dances, and they hung out at our booth trying to buy us more drinks. I sipped on my drink, declining their offers. My brown-eyed admirer leaned in and whispered he liked my hair. His large dark hands motioning toward my wig. I almost lost it. I fought back my laughter, and the idea that my blonde afro wig was nice, but I remained calm. I got Darcie's attention and motioned with a hand gesture toward the women's restroom. We smiled, excused ourselves, and headed straight toward the restroom, but quickly diverted to the exit.

We ran out to the parking lot and jumped into her parent's 1973 Chevrolet Monte Carlo. Darcie hit the gas, and before we knew it, we were on the Nimitz freeway heading south. She noticed a car in her rear-view mirror, speeding toward us, so we pulled off our wigs and I dropped my eyeglasses onto the seat. We fluffed up our hair, running our fingers through each strand. I looked at Darcie and winked. The car approached the driver's side, and it was the two men from the bar. We tried to keep a straight face. They glanced over at us and then sped past. It was hilarious, but at the same time, scary. They had followed us.

There was that guardian angel again. I picked up my blonde afro wig, studied it, and began barking. We both howled and laughed until our guts hurt.

QUADRILATERAL

atie and I had spent our remaining time in Oahu, staying close to our swimming pool at the Paradise Hotel. The surrounding tropical flowers waved a mixed fragrance, including Hawaiian Gardenias' jasmine, mouthwatering Bird of Paradise's citrus scent, and the flowering perfume of Hawaiian Hibiscus. Waterfalls added to the ambiance and cooled the mood as we basked in the soft sunlight.

We ventured out on a couple of excursions. We toured the USS Arizona and walked the memorial which straddled the sunken ship. We stood still and quiet on the sacred ground; it was disheartening. In the shrine room, I was fixed upon the never-ending list of officers and crewmen who remained entombed in the ship. So many lives lost. Their souls seemed to speak in a low hush, penetrating my inner heart. We soon returned to the ship, which transported us. I looked back and gazed vacantly at the shrine while its American flag rippled high upon its mast. It became distant in the waters; much like the Alameda County Courthouse that had once imprisoned my father.

When we returned to the marina, I noticed the inlet of water we had traveled over. The Hawaiian mist and tropical climate lay ahead of us. I looked up and there was my imaginary kite again, flying in the warm tropical breeze. I longed for him, but I refused to allow him into my thoughts. I focused on this moment and then my eyes focused on Katie. She had become very seasick and was turning into shades of white, green, and then white again. She was soon hugging the women's white porcelain shrine below deck. Katie did not travel well on sea.

Back in our hotel room, Katie wanted to rest and talk on the phone with Marco. Marco and his friends were arriving the next day. The same day we would be departing. She was eager to see him, and I was eager to go home. William and James were part of Marco's group. I really did not want to see William ever again.

I convinced Katie for our last night in Hawaii we should participate in a down-to-earth, home-grown, hang-loose, Germaine Luau.

We boarded a bus to the private beach and watched the sun set over the horizon. The ceremony began with the Conch, or a seashell horn, blown by a man dressed in a traditional Hawaiian wrap. We were seated on the ground in front of a long table with very short legs. The music began while they served traditional foods such as: haupia, lomi salmon, poke, opihi and poi. I ordered a mai-tai for us. I bounced from cheek to cheek with the drums. It reminded me of my Brazilian samba experience. Hula dancers made their way onto the stage, while tiki torches were lit and scattered around us. It was the perfect way to end our trip. I was over the moon.

The beep-beep sound of the garbage truck made its way into the back alley. We woke to our early morning wake-up call, compliments of Hotel Paradise. It was our last day, and I wanted nothing more than to pack my suitcase and lay out at the pool. We were scheduled to fly out in the evening, and Katie was expecting Marco around noon. She wanted me out of the room so she could have some privacy with him. "Whatever," is all I could say.

Marco arrived with his entourage of friends, William by his side. I noticed Marco approaching the pool, and I tapped Katie on her arm. "Hey Katie, Marco is coming over," as my hand covered the sun from my eyes. I noticed William scurrying off to their room. *What a loser,* I thought to myself. Marco and Katie returned to our room, and I was finally alone to enjoy the last bit of Hawaiian sun. I was very proud of the golden suntan I managed to get. I had purchased a Hawaiian bikini at the large mall up the street. Katie preferred I wear it, rather than my Tanga. It was a rare day that I could.

I was deep in thought when a slight movement from the clouds cast a shadow over my skin, removing the intense warmth from the sun. My eyes squinted to scan the thirty thousand feet above, hoping to see an airplane passing over. I jumped when I noticed William standing over me with a smile on his face. "Hello, William," I managed.

"Hello, Tess. May I sit down?" he responded.

I nodded and William apologized for standing me up. "I am an ass, and I don't know why I did that, but I am sorry," he said in a low tone. I looked the German man up and down, and my mind drifted to Arthur. How many times did he apologize? How many times do men apologize? Then I looked at William and I felt strengthened.

"Sure, no problem," I responded.

"Can we go for a walk on the beach?" William persisted.

"Sure, why not?" I whispered.

William and I walked on the beach as the afternoon sun settled. He seemed nervous around me, and I was eager to leave. I had lost any feelings I once felt for him. He didn't seem as interesting to me anymore. I watched the waves curl and then break before meeting the shore. I admired the seagulls soaring over the tides. My feet sunk into the cold, damp sand with each step. I imagined a kite flying high into the horizon, and then I closed my eyes as I appeared, bouncing and soaring with the birds. I was happiest when I felt free. Elio continued to tug on that kite string. I glanced at William, and I smiled, knowing William was not holding it.

I said goodbye to William and returned to my room. I tapped on the door and Katie stood peering out at me. She gave me the Katie look, curling up her lip on one side. I took the hint and walked back down to the beach. I sat with my legs tucked under me until the Hawaiian sun set behind the ocean. It was breathtaking. I thought of my uncle's wooden roadrunner; its beak bounced up and down into a glass of water. I raised my arm and reached for my imaginary kite; it seemed to trail behind a jet liner departing from Honolulu.

IN THE WILDERNESS

The airport was busy as Katie and I approached the terminal in our cab. Our tour guide stood nervously waiting for our arrival. We were running late, and our guide worried something had gone wrong. She was relieved when we approached our gate. We still had plenty of time to relax and wait for our boarding call. I glanced at Katie and noticed the sadness in her eyes. She was really falling for Marco, and when Katie fell, she fell hard.

We took our seats on our Western Airlines 747 aircraft. I took my usual seat next to the window and admired the Waikiki coastline illuminated in the distance. We taxied to our departing runway 26R and waited for clearance to take-off. I felt the engines wind up, and I watched the ailerons move up and down. I admired the wing tips and the navigation lights. We lined up on runway 26R and proceeded with the gentle increase of power. I counted the seconds as we forged to lift off and then felt the familiar exhilaration of ascension. We nosed up and our heads slid back, slightly pressing against our head rests. I glanced out the window, and I remember seeing the blackness of night and the twinkling of stars. Honolulu was behind me, and another chapter lay ahead. I took the long expected six-hour flight into consideration and fell back in time. My mind reminisced about days in Bogota, Colombia. I reflected on Samuel Gomez and grinned.

Samuel had telephoned my parents' home shortly after I returned from South America. It was a few weeks after Elio had dumped me for the older woman. I was happy to hear from him. He was visiting his parents in San Leandro and wanted to come by and say hello. "How about I pick you up and we can dine at my parent's home?" he asked. "They would love to meet you, and I would like to meet your family as well?"

I agreed, and within a few hours Samuel was knocking on our side-door entrance. I greeted him with the customary kiss on the cheek and invited him in. My parents sat patiently on the couch, waiting to hear about our encounter and the breathtaking sites in Colombia. Samuel was in his usual attire of blue jeans, flannel shirt, and waffle stomper boots. He was a handsome man with dark hair and those cat eyes. I still felt myself staring into his eyes because they were so unique. He talked, and talked, until the large grandfather clock chimed on the half hour. I motioned to Samuel we should get going. Dinner time approached, and we headed over to his parents' house six city blocks away.

Dinner was fun and very similar to mine growing up. Samuel had two brothers and two sisters. They all joined us at the dinner table, and we talked about our meeting on top of Mount Monserrate in Bogota. We discussed the view from Guadalupe Hill, with the majestic forty-nine-foot-tall statue of *Our Lady of Guadalupe*. The sculptor, Gustavo Arcila Uribe, created the masterpiece in 1946, and it remains standing despite all the earthquakes she encountered.

We shared photos of the small villages and indigenous people occupying them. Samuel had taken many photos during his trip. His family circled back to the subject of two people from the same city in California having a chance meeting on a mountaintop in Colombia. It seemed we were destined to meet, and the thought gave me a feeling of uneasiness that haunted me. I had created an imaginary bubble around me, and the closeness of the opposite sex seemed far from my grasp.

Samuel escorted me home, but before leaving me at my parents' doorstep, he leaned in for a kiss goodnight. I quickly turned my face; his lips lightly brushed my cheek. He gazed at me with those cat eyes. With a slight smile, I leaned down, looking at his boots. "Would you like to go backpacking with me in Yosemite?" he asked. "I am going next weekend and I would love for you to join me."

I hesitated. I had never been backpacking, and going to Yosemite with Samuel might be just what I needed. The thought of fresh air, beautiful mountain peaks, and the wilderness. "Sure, I would love that," I responded.

It wasn't difficult for me to pack. I didn't have much, and Samuel insisted he would handle everything. I just needed to bring a few personal effects and some good hiking boots. I purchased a pair of navy-blue waffle stompers and then visited the Army surplus store in Hayward, California. I bought the Ben Davis, railroad-style bib overalls. They were perfectly comfortable and completely the opposite of anything I would have worn in South America. I was definitely home again. I was different, men were different, and the American lifestyle was different. I embraced the change, at least for this backpacking adventure I did.

In the wee hours of the morning, Samuel picked me up in his green 1972 MG MGB sports car. We loaded up my items into a ten-pound pack and departed for Yosemite National Park. Destination; Tuolumne Meadows. Samuel and I conversed during the three-hour drive about the hike. He intended for us to park in the Meadows and hike ten miles to Crystal Lakes. I had become nervous about the distance. I had walked so much in South America that I convinced myself I could do this. Afterall, I considered myself to be in pretty good shape.

We arrived at the Tuolumne Meadows campground, sitting at eight thousand-six hundred feet above sea level, and he parked his car. The scenic glacial peaks, along with the crisp green bundles of ageless Ponderosa pine trees, gave way to a beautiful rushing stream flowing in an endless hue of blue. We gathered up our packs, and Samuel helped me into mine. I almost fell over backward from the weight. It felt as if the pack weighed more than me, as though I mounted a horse, and the saddle was loose. I had to control rolling over. We headed out to the trail and embarked on our ten-mile hike to Crystal Lakes.

The beginning of this trail was steep, and my pack continued to move back and forth against my waist. It was missing the waist strap, and I had to hold the sides with my hands to keep it steady. It was apparent, quickly, that I was not in good enough shape, and my nicotine habit added to my fatigue. I had to stop within the first half hour and rest. I was out of breath, and my legs were hurting. "Can we break for a smoke?" I asked.

Samuel looked at me and smiled. "I think we should head back to the campgrounds and make camp there for the weekend. I don't think a ten-mile hike was a good idea for your first time."

I was so relieved to hear that. It was obvious I could not backpack, nor did I want to.

Samuel and I set up camp in a pleasant spot near the river lined with granite boulders. It was a beautiful campsite, surrounded by pussy toe plants and stillness. I was happy to relax around the campfire we built. The sun set, and darkness fell upon us. The winds gently awakened the giant Ponderosas and incensed cedars that encircled us. The river's rapid flowing sounds enhanced a romantic setting.

Samuel snuggled up next to me, and with a light wispy touch, he ran his fingers through my hair. He drew me in and held my face. Our eyes met and his soft, delicate kiss embraced mine. My breath had become intense and Samuel scooped me up and carried me to his tent. A soft shimmer of light from his lantern softened the atmosphere. His large hand pulled down on the tent's zipper, closing the deal.

I was suddenly lost in sexual passion. We ripped and pulled at our clothes. It was as though the white leopard had released itself within me. Samuel became my sexual prey, and I was not holding back. I kissed him hard, and he embraced my young tender body. He was built rough, lean, and his wooly chest resembled Sasquatch. His eyes were intense, and he moved with aggression, but he seemed to hesitate as though I may not approve. I did. I wanted him, and I wanted unbridled sex.

Our movements were stormy in the uninhabited wilderness that surrounded us, and we broke the silence. I was no longer a timid, frail, and broken girl from cold concrete and little boxes. I became a woman that night. I was released from my captivity of shame. I was passionate and I loved every minute of it.

We collapsed in the heat of exhaustion, lying naked on top of our sleeping bags. There was no one there to pull me away, no one to lecture me, and no one telling me I had misbehaved. It was just Samuel and I; a man I had met in Bogota, Colombia. He was the guy who lit up my tent that night in the wilds of Yosemite National Park. He had no idea who I was, or where my life had taken me. He didn't grow up knowing me, even though he had lived a stones' throw away. He was perfect, and just what I needed.

Samuel and I spent the next two days barely eating and barely sleeping. Occasionally, we walked to the showers to bathe. Our weekend hike never extended beyond the edge of our campground. We laughed, talked, and engaged in recurrent sex; over and over again. We became comfortable with each other. Our touch began hard and rough but eased into a soft and sensual familiarity.

My guard was down, and he was allowed to see me in the raw, no make-up, no fancy clothes, no high heel shoes. There was no one else camping, except for the bears. They trailed into our camp area with curiosity, or possibly to observe a sense of natural beauty; two humans in the throes of lust.

TURKEY DAY

I surveyed the night sky view outside my airline window. I thought about Samuel one more time. Samuel had dropped me off at my parents' home that late Sunday evening. I waved goodbye as he drove away in his MG sports car. I never saw him again. I would always wonder what became of my Neanderthal man. He had planned on becoming an attorney one day. I hoped he had.

I let out a sigh and looked over at Katie, who was fast asleep. She slept a lot. I took a peek at the stars that sat at the wing tip's edge. My smile quickly dissipated. It was shortly after my weekend at bear country that I had run into Arthur at the drive-in. On my wedding day, my mother whispered in my ear, "Tess, Samuel called a week ago, and I told him you were getting married. He wanted me to extend his best wishes and hoped you would be happy."

I pondered on that for a short time; just long enough to wonder, what if. I pursed my mouth, "Arthur," and then my upper lip curled, just like Katies. I paused, and then my entire face beamed at the thought of Samuel. He was the perfect airship that passed in my night.

I pushed back my seat into a reclining position and grabbed the headset hanging in front of me. I tuned in The Bee Gees' hit song,

"Guilty." I took in the words. How profound, I thought. I had no reason to feel guilty either.

Our long six-hour flight to Oakland, California flew by. I had dozed off, and Katie slept the entire time. As we made our final descent to runway 30, I admired the San Francisco Bay and the twinkling of surrounding neighborhoods. The long straight-in approach allowed time to reminisce. My eyes met the Oakland foothills. It seemed so long ago when I stayed with my Uncle Pete and Aunt Sarah. I was no longer the youthful girl they took in and spoiled. I had become the young woman, who they continued to take in and spoil. They usually invited me and my entire family to their home for Thanksgiving dinner each year.

In my mind, I could still picture us gathered around a long table dusted in white linen, crystal goblets, and fine silverware. Uncle Pete sat at the far end, and Aunt Sarah sat opposite of him with her string of pearls on. It was 1975 and my heart was pining for Elio. My cousin Brigitte was married, and her husband Bernard sat alongside her. He held his 1965 Nikon F2 camera with a zoom lens in my direction. While the family conversed and consumed our Thanksgiving meal, he began snapping photos. I gave him a sheepish smile and admired him and his life that I foresaw.

Bernard and Brigitte were married in 1962, and they made a dashing couple. In June 1964, my family and I were visiting to celebrate the birth of their firstborn. It was a little girl they named Christine. She was a few weeks old when we visited. Brigitte sat at the table, rocking Christine back and forth on her shoulder. Bernard drove a robin's egg blue 1959 Triumph TR-3 convertible sports car. I was so young back then, just about eight years old. I thought the car was really cool.

My aunt needed some whipping cream from the store for our dessert. She asked Bernard if he would run to the market after dinner. I jumped from the table, excited at the opportunity to ride in his car. "Please, please, take me with you!" I begged, looking in his direction. Bernard gave me a nod of approval. It was a bit cold with the convertible top down, but I did not mind. I was driving in a cool car with a cool guy who I thought resembled Sonny Bono. I was on top of the world, or so it seemed at the age of eight.

On our return drive back to my aunt's house, I made my move, "Why don't you leave Brigitte and run away with me, and we could get married?"

With his bushy mustache, and a raised eyebrow, he asked, "What about Brigitte and the baby?"

That was simple. I responded, "Oh, she can have the baby."

He grinned, and then we both chuckled.

Looking down the lens of his camera at that age of nineteen, my sheepish smile was a bit more of an embarrassing smile. I glanced away as I had recalled my proposition to Bernard. He was also the family dentist. He worked so hard to give me that brilliant smile, and I would fall into a stillness in his presence, even when he was filling my back molars with amalgam.

It seemed I was always looking for my knight in shining armor. Cinderella needed to grow up and face reality. There were no knights in shining armor; but there were dentists, and professional baseball players, and lawyers, and perhaps a few airline captains.

WE LANDED WITH THE SQUEAK OF THE SMALL TIRES. MY ATTENTION turned toward Katie and I gave her my thumbs up. She rolled her eyes and reminded me that neither flying nor sailing at sea were on her list of *fun-things-to-do*. We were different in so many ways.

Angie picked us up at the airport, and we spent the night at her home. It was my reminder of years past, and the darkness that lingered.

I was anxious to return to Amador County and Alessandro. He was my new focus and my blind date that awaited me the next week. I was curious about him. My softball coach James insisted he was perfect for me. I had no idea what perfect even looked like, but I was game.

TRYSTED

$\mathcal{I}$ drove to James and Demi's home the following Saturday evening. My skin was still peeling from my Hawaiian suntan. I tried my best to cover up the blemishes on my face with make-up. All week, I had drenched my skin in lotion and aloe vera. It was useless; I was fair skinned and doomed to peel.

I arrived at their small cottage nestled at the south end of Jackson. As I pulled into their driveway, I noticed a patina maroon 1938 Buick Special parked alongside their small green pickup. It was a classic, and I admired the large fenders, suicide doors, hinged hood, and whitewall tires. As I climbed the stairs to their front door, I glanced back one more time and applauded its beauty. I knocked on the front door and Demi greeted me with a big smile. "Come in, Tess, and meet Alessandro," she eagerly motioned.

James sat at the kitchen table conversing with a nice-looking man. He stood and extended a hand. I smiled and nodded my head. No words were spoken as Demi and I joined them at the table. I took my seat and remained guarded as James announced we were going to dinner at our local Italian Restaurant, Vecchio's. My smile lifted when Alessandro announced we were traveling in his 1938 Buick Special. "So that's your car?" I asked.

"Yes, it is," he responded with a wink.

"Cool" I said, and then I conceded, *at least it's not a black Porsche or a convertible sports car.*

Alessandro opened the passenger door, and I sidled in, admiring the mohair bench seat. My eyes scanned the wood grain dashboard. James and Demi sat behind us and chattered from the large bench seat in back. The front bench seat-back fashioned a robe covered grab-rope-bar, framed with brass grommets on each end. It was not only fashionable but was installed in case you needed to grab something during an abrupt stop. There were no seatbelts, and during its date of production they were not required.

We traveled north on Main Street, which merged into Jackson Gate Road. The road's edge followed the deep and narrow opening of the North Fork of Jackson Creek. This area was rich in mining and continues to be regarded as the first mining area in Amador County. The St. Sava Serbian Orthodox Church came into view. It was the first Serbian Orthodox church founded in the western hemisphere. It monumentally stood on the rolling hills, and Alessandro seem excited to share the history with me, especially because I was unfamiliar with this county.

We passed Vecchio's, and continued down the road for a bit of site-seeing. He pointed out the historic Chichizola market, opened in 1849 and closed in 1977. Alessandro rambled on about the family and how they had operated this store for nearly 127 years. We then traveled over a narrow bridge, crossing the creek. The road was lined with flowers, 1800s' style homes, and small trails of orange, yellow, and green foliage. The Kennedy Gold Mine's headframe, erected in 1886, stood in our windshield's view. Alessandro proudly announced how his maternal grandfather had worked in this mine. He went on and on as we made our U-turn at the road's end and proceeded to our dinner house.

Our party of four were seated in a corner booth. A very attractive woman with a black apron approached our table. Alessandro's sister, Francesca, blurted out with a smile, "Hey Alex! Who's your date?"

I stood and reached out my hand and said, "Hi, my name is Tess."

"Nice to meet you, Tess. Hey Jim and Demi! How's it going? I'm your waitress tonight, so please enjoy some bread and dipping sauce while you look over the menu," Francesca said with a wink.

I liked this lady. She seemed genuinely friendly, and I eased myself into the comfortable conversation and company. I was feeling good about my blind date. My eyes were wide open, and I loved everything I was seeing.

We enjoyed a typical Italian style meal, beginning with minestrone soup and salad. Our main course included raviolis. We shared a bottle of red wine, and the four of us seemed to converse and share stories with ease. Our laughter carried into the night. There was a live band in the bar area and the restaurant's dance floor lit up in brilliant colors. Alessandro shared the history of the dance floor. It had been imported from Italy and was the only one in Amador County. We moved to the bar for our after-dinner drinks. We found an empty cocktail table, and I silently chuckled at the thought of a similar table with Arthur. I glanced at the band; it was country music with a bit of rock-n-roll. No one had long hair or fashioned tight gold pants. The thought amused me.

The four of us had trouble talking, the music was too loud, so we took to the dance floor. Alessandro had two left feet. He was a bit off beat but smiled from ear to ear, trying his best. The band belted out Eric Clapton's "Lay Down Sally." I realized some people are not gifted with rhythm, but I didn't mind. I was having a great time and that was all that mattered. The four of us rocked the dance floor that changed colors with each riff.

We returned to our small table, and I leaned into his ear and suggested we go out to the car where we could talk. I really wanted to get to know him more, and it was impossible to talk in the bar. Alessandro did not hesitate. We bolted to the car, leaving James and Demi behind.

"Call me Alex," he said as we scooted into the back seat of his Buick. My ears were humming from the loud music. It was good to be out where we could visit.

"Ok, Alex sounds nice," I said.

"So, you just returned from Hawaii? How was your trip?" he asked.

"It was fun; however, I would have enjoyed it more if my sister wasn't pining over her boyfriend!" I said with a smirk. We talked a bit more and then he made his move.

Alex leaned over and drew the back-window shade down. His dark brown eyes and his well-groomed beard were welcoming. I embraced his touch and the two of us became engrossed in a make-out session.

A tap on the window interrupted us, and we looked up to see Francesca, James, and Demi standing outside the car door. Alex lowered the window and we laughed.

"Hey there, love birds! I am giving Jim and Demi a ride home." Francesca exclaimed.

"Ok, go for it, and we will see you all later!" He leaned over, "Let's get out of here, and go for a drive. I want to show you Sutter Creek," he said.

"Sounds good," I sheepishly smiled. For a moment I felt as though I was misbehaving. Arthur had left his brand and Elio lingered.

We drove through the beautiful town of Sutter Creek, making a turn down East 2nd Street. Alex stopped in front of a large, two-story white home lined with a white picket fence. Its distinguished stance reflected a colonial home from the south. Each window was framed in burgundy wood shutters, and an oval etched glass window was centered in the grand front door. It had a large, sumptuous lawn, which wrapped around the mansion, along with birch trees on one side and fruit orchards on the other. Just down the street was the Catholic church, Our Lady of the Fatima, built in 1861.

"This is the home I grew up in. My parents still live here, and that is the church I was baptized in," he said. My mouth dropped open to a beautiful mansion. I was in awe of the history of this community and the connection Alex had with everything. My connection in the ticky-tacky neighborhood seemed more like cold concrete. I realized we had traveled such different roads in life. I envied his road. We had lived two hours from each other. Yet, it seemed like another country to me; except they spoke English with a bit of Italian here.

We drove back toward Main Street and traveled up a steep road to Tucker Hill and parked. We had a full view of Main Street, admiring the old town mystique and the twinkling of lights. We kicked back in the front seat when Alex made his move again; the intensity heightened. Our breath became heavy, and I relaxed within the compounds of the antique automobile. It was an undeniable feeling of the 1930s. His touch was as tender as the gentle tide passing over a forgotten seashell. The historic town rested under a new moon, while a 1938 Buick swayed under the amber glow of an antique lamp post.

The alcohol was making my head spin. I resisted the urge of letting go and asked if I could smoke.

"I don't smoke, Tess, and I prefer you didn't smoke in my car. How about I take you home and call you in the morning? We can leave your car at Demi's house tonight. It's getting late, and I would feel better if I drove you home. However, before we leave, can I have your phone number?" he asked.

"Sure, but I don't have anything to write with," I said.

"No problem," he responded. Alex leaned toward his windshield, drew in a deep breath, and exhaled into the glass. Then he turned to me and asked, "What's your number?" He raised his index finger and wrote the phone number in the fogged-up area, just above his steering wheel.

I gave him my sister Katie's house phone number. I was spending the night with her since she lived in Jackson, and I would not have to make the long drive home. I was inching closer and closer to moving into town.

We pulled into her driveway. "I will call you in the morning, Tess. We can have brunch and pick up your car!" Alex said with a wink. We kissed goodnight, and I watched as he drove away.

I was no longer standing on the corner of Chapel Avenue and Wiley Boulevard wondering if my husband would come home. I no longer had to endure the coldness that oozed onto the concrete sidewalks of the East Bay. And when you looked around, it always led to a blue mailbox at the end of the street, slithering by the glow of a lonely porch light.

THE HAWK

*I*t was October 18, 1972, and it happened to be the *World Series Week*. The Cincinnati Reds National League Baseball team defeated the Oakland A's in Game 3. It was a shutout; Reds 1 and the A's 0. Tomorrow would be Game 4.

I recalled an invitation I had received, along with a group of girl-friends, to sing at a banquet for the Reds. There were twelve of us named the Untouchables. We sang with a big band similar to Frank Sinatra's or Tony Bennett's band. They had the brass section; trumpets, trombones, French horns, and tubas. There were many drummers, xylo-phones, and a few violins. I recalled band camp and how bad I was in D-Band.

It had been a short drive to the Oakland Hilton, on Hegenberger Road, in my infamous Karmann Ghia. I dressed in my long prom dress; the one I created for Andre on that magical night. It seemed just a few weeks ago he had left. But, as time has its way, I was on my own. I pulled into the parking lot, near the banquet room, and positioned my car facing downhill (just in case). I was nervous about singing for the Reds; that just doesn't happen every day.

I remember entering the grand room and took my position with the others, front stage. We practiced a few songs to warm up. The lights were dimmed, and people started to arrive. My eyes scanned the room, hoping to see someone I might recognize. The lead vocalist belted out the Carpenters hit song "Close to you," and we sang backup. We sounded pretty good, at least good enough to entertain the Cincinnati Reds.

One by one, the players, along with Al Davis and Ben Davidson from the Oakland Raiders, entered the room. It was Clay Carroll who caught my eye, or should I say, I caught his? He was their right-handed pitcher and was nicknamed the Hawk.

In between songs, I would notice the Hawk checking me out. I would blush and look the other way. During our breaks, we were instructed to mingle with the players. Our job was not only to entertain them, but to distract and entice them. I was too young to understand the strategy here, but in time I came to realize why we were really here.

The Hawk zeroed in on me as I walked around the tables of athletes. He introduced himself and offered to buy me a drink. I was sixteen years old, and definitely too young for alcohol. But the Hawk was kind and bought me a Shirley Temple. I sat down at his table and we conversed with each other. He asked me lots of questions about my age, my life, my career goals, and what I would do in a couple of years. He seemed content talking with me, and I with him. After a couple of drinks, I excused myself and continued to mingle with other patrons.

I noticed a couple of my girlfriends getting cozy with a few of the players. I observed them leave the banquet hall and walk toward the hotel. I ignored them, and as I turned to continue my walk, I ran into Ben Davidson. We both chuckled, and I looked up at him in amazement. He was so tall; six-foot-eight-inches, to be exact. He motioned me over to a photo shoot area. I stood proudly and anxiously, having my picture taken alongside him. I felt like a child standing next to him. I thanked him and turned to notice the Hawk. His mouth gestured for me to join him at his table again. I sauntered over and another Shirley Temple awaited me. "Can you autograph my cocktail napkin?" I asked him.

"You bet!" he replied.

"How about a dance, Tess?" he asked.

"Absolutely," I responded.

We made our way on to the dance floor and danced slowly to the music of our knock-off band. The Hawk was a smooth dancer, and the dances were many. I was lost in the night and the music. It took me back to the night I had with Andre, and I struggled to forget.

It wasn't long before the crowds left, and I became tired. The Hawk offered to walk me out to my car, and I accepted. As we approached my 58 Karmann Ghia, I observed a couple more of my girlfriends meandering toward the hotel with more of the players. I raised my eyebrow at the Hawk. "It was a pleasure to meet you, Mr. Carroll," I said.

"It was all mine," he said with a wink.

"Good luck at game four tomorrow!" I said, and I drove off. The Hawk just eyed me as I made my way out of the parking lot and onto Hegenberger Road. I glanced in the direction of the Oakland Airport and observed the jetliners ascending into the night sky. I tuned in my radio to Lou Rawls singing "Down Here on the Ground" and sunk into his words. I chuckled at the thought of the Hawk in flight, and then I was relieved my car had fired up without a hiccup. The Hawk flew into my life, making a gentle dive, and then soared out; just like everyone else.

The Reds lost game four the next day. Oakland's victory was three and the Reds two. I often wondered if the outcome would have been different, if we had not been invited at the last minute. I've heard of such things, but at the time I was naïve enough to think we were invited because we were good performers.

"Good performers, I whispered." I guess we were, after all we performed for the Cincinnati Reds American League Baseball team; in more ways than one.

IT WAS A FOND MEMORY THAT HAD LONG BEEN FORGOTTEN. I SUNK BACK on my sister Katie's couch, my head resting upon a welcoming pillow. I reached over and flipped off the lamp light, and fell, once again from emotional exhaustion.

PORTMANTEAU

*I*t was a beautiful morning when Alex arrived the following day for brunch. My sister Katie's doorbell rang, and as I entered her living room, I noticed Alex peering in from the door's windowpane. It was a small window, just high enough for a tall person to peak through. I snickered at seeing his eyebrow above his dark brown eyes, while the rest of his face was hidden behind the door panel.

Alex and I drove to Demi and James's home to pick up my car. Luckily, they were not home, so I didn't have to explain my absence to their inquisitive minds. After dropping my car at Katies, we drove to Rancho Murieta, California. We arrived at the Murieta Golf and Country Club. Each Sunday they hosted a brunch. Alex and I were seated at a table adorned in fine linen, beautiful fine china, and crystal stemware. There was romance in the air. We began with a bottle of champagne followed by eggs benedict along with salads of all varieties. Soft piano music played in the background and the two of us enjoyed our intimate hour, getting to know each other. Alex went down smooth, like a fresh glass of water ready to quench my thirst. I immersed myself in this sensual flowing stream. I wanted so much to feel loved.

We finished brunch and drove to Amador City, arriving at Alex's home. Showers fell, and I recalled the smell of fresh rain as it settled on the old cobblestones of Bogota, Colombia. I followed him, hand in hand, as we approached his front porch. It had the character of the typical 1800s home. The porch wrapped around the front and an old metal porch swing with soft red cushions sat on its perch. The old entry door with a cut-glass window framed the ornate brass doorknob and large keyhole below. Alex allowed me to enter first as I scanned the fourteen-foot walls.

The home welcomed a charm from years past. I remember feeling as though I had entered another period, just like his car. Alex's home was decorated with antique furniture, including an old dining room table and matching buffet from the 30s. He walked over to the stereo and picked out an album. His selection impressed me as Leon Russell began singing "Lady Blue."

Alex removed his jacket, and then mine. He led me into the living room area and took one hand in his and danced slowly with me. His movements were awkward, but I followed and slowly relaxed. He had an intensity in his dark brown eyes. He leaned in to kiss me, and I welcomed his touch, his eagerness, and his warm full lips. He reminded me of Elio, and yet his age and stature were completely different. Alex was one-year-old than me, and he carried himself with the awkwardness of a stat-keeper at a high school football game. He was not even close to being the star quarterback, but intellectually he soared above all the players.

The stereo flipped albums, and Joe Cocker's "With a Little Help from My Friends" began to play. I remember commenting to Alex on how much I like this song. He asked if I knew the artist and I hesitated, not able to recall Joe Cocker for the life of me.

Alex snickered and said, "How can you like a song that much, and not know who is singing it?"

I was embarrassed and suddenly felt intimidated by him. I detected a hint of arrogance, and I fought to ignore his comment.

We snuggled on his antique couch, and Alex fell fast asleep. His light snoring lulled me into deep thought. I wondered how I would fit into this man's life. He seemed so grounded and his roots sunk deep within the community. There was no longer a feeling of cold concrete or dark streets leading to blue mailboxes. I lay hopeful next to Alex, but I wondered if my interest had more to do with security than love. Love was something I had locked up within my heart and letting go of that would be challenging. I thought of Luis in Brazil and his words in my ear; "I cannot pass one minute without you." I longed for the words; the words spoken in Portuguese. I recalled Andre's promise to marry me, and then his broken promise. My love for Elio. My love for someone who admired my ass more than my soul. I needed to find my way home. "Home?" I whispered, and then I looked around Alex's house.

TINY TOES

Ten tiny toes–I counted. It was August 9, 1986; exactly twelve years since Richard Nixon resigned as President of the United States that my Isabella Caminetti was born. She had copper red hair and her eyes were brown, just like her dad. Alex and I had made it through the labor and delivery phase of childbirth. I held my daughter in awe of her beautiful tender skin and small hands. She immediately drew to my breast and began feeding. I was captivated by her beauty. Alex had fallen asleep in the chair beside my hospital bed. I sunk my head back against my pillow and reminisced about the past six years.

ALEX HAD SLOWLY SLIPPED INTO BEHAVIOR THAT RESEMBLED ARTHUR'S, but without the violent outbursts. He would disappear for days, not calling and ignoring my attempts to call him. We didn't own answering machines yet, and life depended on being in the right place at the right time. Or the wrong place at the wrong time.

Christmas 1980 had slithered its way into our relationship. Alex arrived one evening with a freshly cut Christmas tree. I was moved by his gesture, but in the weeks to follow there was only silence from him.

Christmas slithered out, and I pined over not seeing or hearing from him. Alex had his usual explanations for not calling. He was busy with work, or he was busy with family, or he was sick, or whatever. It did not matter to me anymore. The bottom line: he was busy.

And then, he called, "Would you like to go to a New Year's Eve party with me, Tess? I can pick you up after work around 7:00 pm?" Alex suggested. "I have missed you and would love to bring in the New Year alongside you!"

I hesitated, thinking to myself, *how can I turn him down?*

New Year's Eve arrived, and I dressed for an evening of celebration. I waited for Alex to arrive in anticipation of welcoming the New Year. I was startled when my phone rang. When I answered it, Alex apologized. "I am really sick, Tess. I have a fever and body aches. I am going to stay home and try to sleep this off. I am so sorry to cancel at the last minute, but I felt sick this morning, and it only became worse as the day set in. How about I call you in the morning?"

"Sure, is there anything I can do for you?" I asked.

"No, Tess. I will have some soup and go straight to bed" and just like that Alex hung up the phone.

The next morning, my sister Katie phoned. She and Marco had attended the same New Year's Eve party Alex had invited me to. "Where were you?" Katie asked.

"I was home and went to bed just after midnight. Alex was sick so we couldn't make it," I responded.

"That's interesting, because Alex was there with another woman!" she briefed me. I thought of William and Kathie's phone call that following morning. She reminded me of the front page of the town's newspaper. "Extra, extra. Read all about it!" I conjured the thought as I raised my upper lip.

I was feeling like the brunt of a bad joke. I was embarrassed and humiliated. I felt the rage within me rise. I flashed back to throwing Arthur on the front lawn and beating him to a pulp. "Thanks for letting me know" I hushed and then hung up the phone.

I immediately phoned Alex. His sleepy voice answered the phone. I hollered at him and shouted what an asshole he was. He was quiet and listened while I ranted and raved. When I finished, there was dead silence on the phone. I realized he had hung up on me.

ISABELLA AND HER TINY TOES WIGGLED. I HELD HER FOOT IN MY PALM AND it meshed perfectly against my middle finger. They were the same length. Then, I looked at Alex passed out in the chair. It had been a long night, and an even longer road getting here.

STRING THEORY

*I*t was in late January 1981 when life threw me a curve ball. I was six weeks late for my monthly menstrual cycle. I was a bundle of nerves when I drove to Alex's home in Amador City. I stopped at the local pharmacy and purchased a pregnancy test. I pulled up in his driveway and made the long walk to his front door. I stood on his front porch, knocked, and waited while trying to catch my balance.

Alex was surprised. With a slight hesitation, he invited me into his home. I seated myself on his couch and let out a deep breath. "We need to talk," I said as calmly as possible. "I bought a pregnancy test kit."

Alex just stood staring at me with his mouth open. "How did that happen? I thought you used your diaphragm every time?" he questioned.

"I did, but the doctor said it *isn't* 100% fool-proof, and I am never this late; except for that one time in Brazil," I reiterated.

I walked to the bathroom and followed the directions. I had to urinate in a cup and then dip a test strip into it. I joined Alex on the couch and waited the ten long minutes as instructed. We sat. He clasped and unclasped his hands, and sat still, avoiding conversation. After the necessary time passed, our eyes met in disbelief. It was positive. I wanted to throw-up.

This was not in my plan, but then again, what was? My body felt changed, and I knew in my heart this was a bad road to go down. I glanced at Alex's oozing disapproval from his eyes and his furrowed brow dropped. He looked down at the floor, and then with all the breath it took to fill his lungs, he seemed to lunge at me with his words, "I can't support you with a baby, Tess. I'm not ready to be a father, and I certainly am not in a position to have a child. You have to abort it, and I will back you up financially on this."

My eyes welled up with tears, and I felt alone and physically blasted. I told myself to be brave, to be quiet, to walk away from this man, and I would vow to never see him again. All my hate for mankind stirred inside of me. I was trapped, and I only had myself to blame. I was intimate with a man who clearly did not love me. How could he? Shame set in, and I wanted to curl up into a ball and bounce away.

"Goodbye," I said as I stood to leave. "I will be in touch with the details in a few days. I will go through with the abortion, but I want nothing to do with you ever again."

I made my way down the two-lane highway of 49. I drove without thought or vision of the broken white lines that separated me from the oncoming traffic. It was as though I was a programmed driving robot. I had no memory of who I passed or what I passed or how the tree's limbs moved from side to side, depositing leaves along the way. I mechanically drove further south until a sign caught my attention. It read, "Westover Field Airport." I made the left turn.

I maneuvered up the winding road which led to the top of a plateau. I noticed the small office ahead and a large sign with a Chevron logo. I pulled to a stop in the parking area and fixed my eyes on the rows of small airplanes tied down in the overnight transient area. I shut down my engine and blankly stared ahead. "Dear Lord, forgive me," I whispered, and then I broke down.

I felt useless and hopeless. I felt numb from the relentless ringing in my ears. My grandfather's words haunted me; "You're not a virgin and I won't waist my money taking you to a doctor to find out. You can't be trusted around boys, and especially your cousins." The motel room of hateful words encompassed me.

I sat back and gazed at the airport's American flag that rippled in the breeze. I was reminded of my father's eyes peering down at me through the small window opening of his cell door. My innocent years of three felt the shame in his eyes and the rejection in his words; "Why did you have to bring her here?"

I reflected on the linoleum floor in San Leandro, and the taste of blood in my mouth. I was frightened then, and I am frightened now. I feared the taste of blood again, and I feared the remnants of darkness in which I was about to enter.

I called my girlfriend, Susan Sanders, for help. Susan was the 2nd runner-up in the beauty pageant and a dear friend. I explained my situation, and she jumped in to help. "I'll handle it, Tess. You don't need to worry. Drive down here to my home. You can stay a few days and rest," she reassured me.

Susan lived in Hayward, and it was only a two-hour drive. I left the next morning and met Susan at the medical office. She sat in the waiting room alongside me until my name was called. "It will be alright, Tess. I am here for you," she said with a smile.

The sterile room and table were cold and unfeeling. I looked about the small chamber made of tile, cement walls, and bright lights. I laid on top of the crinkled paper, staring at the ceiling, wondering if I had made the right decision. A nurse entered the room and asked me repeatedly, "Are you sure, Tess?"

My head signaled an approving nod, while my eyes remained fixed on the ceiling. Visions of a roadrunner teetering up and down into a glass of water entered my sound of silence.

A doctor entered the room. His questions were callous and continued like a broken record on my father's Hi-Fi-stereo. "You will feel some pressure, Tess, and then it will be over." I waited for the pain in which I deserved.

I was a horrible person; I told myself.

The procedure began, and I could hear a device that sounded too much like my vacuum cleaner, which was neatly tucked away in the hall closet. *That's where I belonged*, I thought, *put away in the hall closet.*

The pressure began, and the pain intensified. I could feel the life inside of me getting sucked out and into a black hole. My body collapsed, and I remember a buzzing sound in my ears, and then my brain, and then my eyes. My eyelids closed, as did my desire for life.

It was over. The doctor squeezed my leg and walked away. No words were spoken. Susan appeared within minutes and sat beside me. She held my hand. We sat in the coldness of an empty room and the infinite small particles within vibrating strands disbanded into space.

REFRESHING TIDES

$\mathcal{I}$n the early spring of 1981, I *jumped* at the opportunity to leave Amador County. I moved to Avila Beach, California. It was a beautiful town along the coast, nestled just over the hill from San Luis Obispo.

Juan and I had reconnected. He was the X-ray technician who insisted I leave Arthur back in the Bay Area. One random day, I received a phone call from him, and he invited me to Monterey for a weekend. Juan bought a round trip air fare ticket, and I departed from Sacramento Metro Airport on the short flight. Upon landing, I noticed Juan standing in the terminal waiting to greet me. He was a nice-looking Hispanic man who resembled Al Pacino. Juan held a bouquet of flowers in hand. I embraced him and we meandered out of the terminal to the parking area. I noticed a big black limousine waiting outside, and the driver motioned us toward him. Juan smiled and whispered, "I told you to leave him. I can make you happy!"

We drove to Juan's condominium in Avila Beach. It was a beautiful drive up the coastal highway of California, and we shared a bottle of champagne as Juan pointed out the area's scenic highlights. The limousine driver inched up the winding drive to the beautiful look out point of Avila Bay Inn. Our destination was just beyond the inn. The small town lights twinkled around us, and the old town's pier trailed 1,685 feet to the bay. After dropping my bags at the condo, Juan and I walked down to a small café on the beach for dinner. It was a favorite for him, and they specialized in seafood. I'm not sure if it was the champagne, the wine, or the stage he set, but I became limp like a boiled spaghetti noodle. It was fast, and it was incandescent.

We ended our evening in Juan's bed, right where he wanted me. He was smooth, relentless, and calculating. He knew what he was doing, and he took pleasure in having the upper hand. "Leave Amador County, Tess. Move to Avila Beach and live with me. I will provide for you, take care of you, and you will never have to work. I have always loved you, even from afar, and now you are here with me. Love me, Tess, and stay forever," he insisted.

I lay beside Mr. Juan Pacino and pondered his proposal. I needed to leave Alex behind; he had disappointed me in so many ways. So, I seized the opportunity to go. I glanced over at Juan and responded, "Yes, I will leave and move in with you."

Juan was working at Diablo Canyon Nuclear Power Plant. He had made a career change from X-ray technician to industrial X-ray operations. He was part of the power plant's construction phase, and Juan was an intricate part of the quality control department. The money was really good, and he had made many friends in the area.

We settled into a fun lifestyle, jet setting around the surrounding towns. Juan flew a hang-glider, which made for an interesting gathering on nearby hilltops, and spectacular views of the Pacific coastline. We spent many weekends at Shell Beach and Oceano while Juan at every opportunity snapped photos of me with his 35mm Minolta camera. I would settle down in a meadow of California poppies, or gaze at the ocean from the surrounding cliffs. Occasionally we would rent a Sand Odyssey and drive through the sand dune highways of Pismo Beach. They were beautifully lined with eucalyptus trees, which attracted thousands of the Monarch butterflies each year.

Then things dramatically changed. Juan was offered a position at a nuclear power plant in Washington State. It was under construction in the Tri-City area of Richland, Kennewick, and Pasco. We rented a big moving truck and headed to Bumfuck, Egypt.

It was a new chapter, and an uncharted, drab, camouflaged region for me. We moved to the Hanford area and Juan took up employment with WPPSS (Washington Public Power Supply System) in their quality control department. It was a lucrative move for Juan, but a very lonely move for me. I was suddenly surrounded by miles of nothing and remained secluded in the compounds of our luxurious apartment. While the complex provided all the amenities you could ask for (swimming pool, full gym, recreation room, salons, and spas), it was hundreds of miles away from California, and I knew in my heart I was a California girl. It wasn't long before I applied for a job at the construction site. Juan was opposed at first, but I needed to be busy, and I wanted to feel useful.

I was immediately hired for a position in the document control department. They paid extremely well, and before long (my backpack loaded with documents), I was walking around the construction site updating blueprints, work orders, and revisions, more revisions, and more revisions for engineers, electricians, plumbers, and X-ray technicians. I entered the many construction trailer offices, some very remote work areas, and frequented the nuclear power plant library. It was expansive and sometimes eerie.

One afternoon, I ventured down into the nuclear power core. The construction workers were eager to help me scurry through a small opening and scale a ladder down into a large dome shaped room. I scribbled my name on the inside of the core wall, together with a thousand others. It was daunting, and I recall feeling very claustrophobic. I became known as the strange woman who entered each day, changed documents in books or blueprints in hanger racks, and then would leave without saying a word. Not too many people talked to me; they seemed to observe me from afar. I was a mystery to them. I liked it that way, and I played along with the mystique. Juan and I passed each other on occasion. He would give me a nod with a look like he was undressing me, followed by a wink.

One evening, our telephone rang. It was during our dinner hour, and Juan answered it. "It's Alex," he scowled.

I rose to answer the call. Juan stomped out of our apartment in a fury, slamming the door and carrying his bicycle in hand. I took the receiver, standing in the kitchen dazed and immobilized.

"Hi Alessandro, why are you calling? You realize I am living with another man?" I mumbled.

"Join me in Hawaii. I am flying out next week, and I will buy your airfare, hotel, and anything else you need. Do you hear me, Tess? Leave him. I miss you and I love you. Come home," Alex insisted.

Memories of Alex and I dancing on the antique rug in his antique home rolled into my mental frame. I could almost hear Leon Russell singing "Back to the Island" while Alex rambled on and on.

UNOCCUPIED SPACES

*I*t was October 8, 1982, when Alex and I said our wedding vows. The Caminetti Family Home was the perfect setting for our ceremony. We stood under the three birch trees, just beyond the steps of the French doors leading from their formal dining room. The cool weather was accompanied by a slightly warm breeze from the Indian summer haze. Alex insisted we only invite our immediate family, "Tess, if I invite all my friends, the entire community would be there. I can't have hundreds at our wedding, and I want our wedding to be a private affair."

How could I argue with that? Arthur and I had our big wedding fiasco, and I sensed impropriety at the notion of a second time around.

I RETURNED TO AMADOR COUNTY IN THE LATE SUMMER OF 1981. JUAN went back to Avila Beach, and I went my way. I did not go to Hawaii with Alex. That would have been ridiculous; however, it was a bittersweet break up with Juan. He deserved someone to love him, and as hard as I tried, my heart belonged to someone or somewhere else. Love was complicated, and Alex pursued me with such intensity. It was the intensity I had yearned for from Elio.

I found a one-bedroom apartment in Jackson and returned to my life in Amador County, working at my parents' accounting office. Life was good, or so it seemed. Alex and I spent every moment together. We both enjoyed theatre in the Sacramento Metropolis, outdoor concerts at the Concord Pavilion, and trips to Lake Tahoe with overnights at the casinos, or hanging out on the beach. We spent time at Silver Lake, a large lake near Kirkwood Ski Resort. We sailed in Alex's small sailboat and frequented the Vecchio Cabin. The Caminetti Family and the Vecchio Family had a long history together, and their cabin became a warm welcome from the Jackson climate.

Months passed as we settled into a relationship again. Alex and I bounced around between his house and my apartment. I became open to the idea of loving him and supporting his desire to be with me. I let my guard down, and although I was careful to use protection during our time together, my reputation as a "fertile sister" preceded me. I was late, again. My inner self knew, without a doubt, that I was pregnant. I purchased a home test kit, and behind closed doors I confirmed my deepest fear.

It was so difficult to break the news to him. His reaction did not surprise me, although it deeply disappointed me–one more time. I arranged for him to drive me to and from Sacramento's Planned Parenthood office. I was numb, and the reality of another aborted pregnancy was more than I could comprehend. I was uninformed, ill prepared, and uneducated as to the emptiness this would leave within me.

I crawled onto the table within the cold, sterile room. I lay motionless as people spoke to me; their words sounded like Charlie Brown's teacher with a WA-WA-WA tone. My embarrassment amplified, and the tears streamed down my face. I felt hatred toward Alessandro, and I hated myself for allowing this to happen again.

Thoughts of leaving reappeared in my mind and I wanted to run–to fly. I wanted to return to my sanctuary and admire the seagulls flying above. I wanted to be on the park bench watching the jets take off and land at Oakland International Airport. I wanted to be anywhere but here.

Alex parked outside, waiting for me. The nurse escorted me to the car, and I crawled into the front seat, mentally and physically filled with pain. I told myself to never date this man again. We were too good at fertility and horribly irresponsible with the consequence.

Weeks passed, and I went into isolation. I avoided people. I took my phone off the hook and I withdrew. Susan Sanders had given up on our friendship. She could not forgive Alex, and consequently she could not forgive me. Simon and Garfunkel's "Sounds of Silence" played in my head. I contemplated my life, my value, my behavior, and then I prayed. I prayed that someday I could forgive myself.

"MARRY ME, PLEASE, TESS!" ALEX SAID. IT WAS MONTHS SINCE MY RETURN from depravity.

"I never want to see you again!" I protested over the phone with him. "I hate you, Alex, and I want nothing to do with you. I have been through a horrendous experience, and need I remind you, not once but twice! Where were you? Huh, Alessandro? Where were you when I crawled onto those cold tables and had innocent lives sucked out of me? Where were you? You were up at the Vecchio's cabin, and then you were having lunch with your sister, Amalia!" I screamed through the phone receiver.

I hung up the phone, circled around the kitchen table as the phone began to ring again.

I picked up the receiver, and Alex hollered, "Don't hang up on me, Tess. Please listen. I am sorry, and I love you. What does it take for you to believe me? I want you in my life and I want to marry you. I made a mistake; can you forgive me?"

There it was. That question of *forgiveness*. I was raised to forgive. All those years at church instilled the act of forgiving. None of us are perfect, least of all me. I was a sinner and now am I being tested? Is this a moment of redemption for me... for us?

"You can't even propose properly, Alex. If you are that serious, then prove it to me!" I said with a second slamming of the phone receiver. I glared at the white phone on my kitchen wall. I hesitated, and then I removed the phone from the wall jack and threw it on the floor. No one would be able to call me... no one.

I slipped back into my bed in my one-bedroom apartment, pulled the covers over my head, and sobbed. My heart was bleeding, as was the rest of my body from the cold, sterile, and familiar calamitous procedure.

My slumber had been interrupted by a pounding on my front door. I raised from bed, only to find Alex standing there. He stood wide-eyed and terrified. He inched his way in, noticing my phone on the floor. "Please, Tess. Let's talk this over," he persisted.

We sat at my kitchen table. He held a calmness in his voice, sincerity in his eyes, and sadness on his face. I listened as he carefully, cunningly, and meticulously begged for my forgiveness. He seemed haunted by his actions, and I was haunted by mine. And then he did the unthinkable; he knelt down on one knee, pulled out a ring from his pocket, and proposed.

"Please marry me, Tess. I will take care of you. I will never harm you, and I will always love you," he gently whispered.

I was speechless, stunned, shell-shocked, as though the life in me marched its way in and out, and back out again. "No, I won't. I can't, Alex. I can't marry you. No, please don't ask this of me!" I cried. "When I needed you, you turned your back on me," I said.

"Just think it over, Tess. You don't have to decide right now. I will leave you this ring and you can let me know," and with that, he stood and walked out.

I DO – I DON'T

*I*t had been two weeks since the big question was asked. I continued thinking about his proposal, working in silence and reflection. When I returned home in the evenings, I would take the engagement ring out of my dresser drawer and admire it. It was a beautiful platinum setting with a large round cut diamond encircled by six pear-shaped diamonds, forming a flower. The ring fit perfectly and I pondered whether that was a good sign. "No," I would say to myself, and then I replaced the ring in my dresser drawer, and slammed it shut.

I traveled to my father and mother's home for some much-needed advice. I explained how unreliable Alex was. I shared with my parents his disloyalty and thoughtlessness toward me. I was confused, and I looked to them for comfort, or security, or strength. I had made so many mistakes and wanted them to tell me which direction I should take?

With my mother sitting next to my father's side and much to my surprise, the words escaped, "Marry him, Tess. You will never go without. He will always provide for you." My father continued talking, but a heavy fog fell over me, much like the fog sneaking its way across the Golden Gate Bridge. I was lightheaded and all of his words embedded into my cerebral mass.

After many days of contemplation, I finally made the drive to Alex's home. I arrived at the familiar residence burrowed in the trees that surrounded it. I knocked gently on his front door and waited. I was hoping he would not be home, but the door opened, and I entered his living room and into his awaiting embrace.

"I missed you, Tess. Have you decided yet?" his eyes drooped. His brow, along with his puppy-dog brown eyes, tugged at my heartstrings.

Was that braid in my heart slowly coming apart? "Yes, I have decided" I said.

"Let's retire to the other room and talk." I followed Alex into his kitchen and took a seat at the table.

"I can't marry you, Alex." I began, "I am returning this ring to you with my sincerest regret." I placed the ring on the table.

Alex teared up. I wasn't expecting this. His tears turned into a torrential downpour. He covered his eyes with his hands. I could not bear seeing him this way. I stood and put my arms around him. I tried to comfort him, but he insisted. "Please, Tess. Don't do this to me. I am so sorry I hurt you. I need and love you, please marry me!"

I was stunned, tongue-tied, and had feelings of compassion. There it was. I looked into his eyes and I finally spoke. "Ok, Alex. I will marry you."

"Really?" Alex said with a sheepish look.

"Yes, I will marry you, Alessandro Caminetti." I cradled him in his antique kitchen chair, surrounded by his antique kitchen relics.

I moved into Alex's home, following the advice of his parents. "No need to pay rent for two places when you are getting married!" his mother reassured. I vacated my apartment and vacated my single life. I moved into the world of marriage, and this time I was optimistic that Alex would honor his commitment to me.

I remained the hopeless optimist. I clung to love, faith, and family. I began settling in with a touch of me. I adored the antiques that decorated the historical family home. I was free to decorate the interior of the home, while he spent hours maintaining a vegetable garden and the demanding landscape. In the evenings, following a long week, Alex and I would dance to the sweet tunes of Frank Sinatra or Boss Skaggs. That was my expertise. I would lead him, and he became more graceful with his moves. His awkward tempo gently relaxed into a left and right pace. He listened patiently as I repeated, "One, two, three, one, two three."

We had a very welcoming surprise with the arrival of Sofia and Luiza from Brazil. They traveled to visit and stay with us. They were to spend a week in California, and I was elated.

I drove the three of us to San Francisco for shopping and time in the city. We stayed for two nights. Lexie offered her home in the East Bay for overnight accommodations. It was good to see her again. It had been so long. We dined and caught up.

The next day the three of us rode the infamous cable cars, starting in Ghirardelli Square and ending in Union Square for shopping. We went to Macy's department store, which is four levels, and spent hours shopping. I found the perfect ivory tiered-lace-pyramid skirt with a matching blouse. The ivory lace blouse had cap sleeves, bridal button loops down the entire back, and silk piping around the neckline. I stood in the dressing room, turning around and around. It was perfect for my wedding day; not too fancy, not white, and not at all traditional.

We enjoyed the four level Gap complex across the street from Nordstrom's on Market Street. I purchased a new pair of black Timberland hiking boots at Nordstrom's. I had worn out my old pair and loved the new style. I giggled at the thought of wearing them with my two-piece wedding gown. We grabbed a taxi and took in lunch at the North Beach Restaurant. We ended our day walking down Broadway Street. The city lights at night reminded me of Las Vegas, Nevada. Broadway was lined with bars, restaurants, and nightclubs. We passed by Finocchio's Club–a San Francisco landmark.

A man standing outside one of the neighboring clubs lured us in. It was a male strip club, and my Brazilian friends had no idea. We were seated at a small cocktail table. The music began with "I'm Gonna Love You" by Barry White; then out came our first of many male dancers. He was young, blonde, tone, and he immediately zeroed in on us. Before I knew it, he took off his clothes and danced on our table! I was amused, and Sofia and Luiza's jaws dropped. They sat wide-eyed and dumbfounded. We stuffed money in the dancer's G-string. And within minutes, all three of us were engaged in the performance, dancing with each dancer as they made their way over to our party of three. It was a perfect ending to a perfect day.

As we made our drive over the Bay Bridge, I noticed the undulations along with the breaks of water beneath us. I rolled down my car window and took in the salted air, and then we all howled. There was a full moon that night. It was a moon that encapsulated both Brazil and America, connecting them together–so did my heart.

The following afternoon Sofia, Luiza, and I drove back to Amador City to continue our visit at my new home and to spend time with my parents in the Sierra Nevada Mountains. That is when I became nervous.

We arrived in the late afternoon. Alex wasn't home yet, and the drapes were drawn. As we entered the house, we all noticed the two wine glasses on the kitchen counter. Alex's king size bed had been stripped, and the bedding was in the dryer. As I walked into the bathroom, I saw the trash had been taken out. The remnants of melted candle wax added to the sense of infidelity that lingered in the air. My stomach churned, and my Brazilian friends raised their eyebrows. I walked over to the stereo. *Winelight* by Grover Washington Jr. rested upon its turntable.

I excused the obvious with my friends, out of sheer embarrassment. They repacked, and we headed to Pioneer. No words were spoken, and I was riddled with confusion. I wanted so much to believe that I was wrong. I wanted the life he had to offer, and I wanted to settle down. I was tired of running, and then I remembered my father's words.

After leaving Sofia and Luiza at my parent's home, I returned to my new home with Alex. As I entered the house, I confronted him. He sat on our sofa. His excuse was so unbelievable, yet I convinced myself to believe him. He clung to his story.

"I came home and was in the mood for soft music and some wine, Tess. I didn't realize I had left my glass of wine in the bathroom, so I retrieved another glass. That's why there are two sitting on the kitchen counter. I had eaten dinner at Burger King, and later that night I was sick with food poisoning. I thought I was going to pass gas, but I had an accident in the bed. I had to wash the sheets; it was awful. I vomited in the bathroom trash can, so I had to take it out because of the smell. I realize it looks bad, but really, Tess! I would not do that to you. You must believe me."

"I do," I repeated to John C. Begovich, former state senator of California. John was a personal friend of the Caminetti family and was more than happy to officiate our wedding ceremony. John had quite the past, having served in World War II and receiving three Purple Hearts. He became one of our County Supervisors and worked alongside my sister Katie. I stood before John, who happened to be a very fast speaker. I barely understood him, and before I knew it, under the three birch trees in Sutter Creek, Alex and I were married.

The families gathered around us and all were cheering us on as man and wife. I was pensive and somewhat detached. I had married for the second time, knowing this man had rejected me more than once. I watched as my family conversed with his. I noticed the smiles on all their faces, and I tried to brush thoughts of my past away from the moment. I had become deeply invested in this family. I was sucked into the Italian traditions, which reminded me too much of my Brazilian family. I loved them and I wanted to be a part of this way of life. Elio had another, Andre had another, and Alex persisted to the extent of an unremitting rainstorm.

We paraded through town in Alex's 1938 Buick Special to Vecchio's Italian Restaurant for our wedding reception. It was an intimate affair, and the Vecchio Family hosted a private dinner for our families. We were surrounded by our loved ones, Italian food, champagne, and good wine.

Alex's father, Angelo, and his mother Alma had flown in from New York, after visiting family in Queens. Angelo's brother owned and operated an Italian bakery, and insisted on baking a Napoleon cake for us. I could only imagine how comical they looked carrying a big sheet cake onto the airplane. My new father-in-law guarding the Napoleon with his life.

My father and mother held their champagne glasses up for a toast. It was the first time I observed them drinking alcohol. It brought a smile to my face, and for a fleeting moment, I felt a bit of relief. Maybe Father was correct. Maybe this man would take good care of me.

I turned my thoughts to the male dancer in San Francisco. He was so handsome, young, and seemed so innocent. I wondered why he chose that path in life. What story did he have? What secrets are buried beneath that white smile, blonde hair, and tone body? And then I thought of Alex and his food poisoning. With one eyebrow raised, I disposed of the true story.

BELLA

*A*lex carried Isabella Caminetti out of the hospital. She was tiny and her copper red hair draped across her small forehead. She had a brow like her dad. Alex transferred Isabella into her infant car seat, and I took my usual place in the front seat. We left the hospital in our red 1982 Mercedes Benz 300SD. Our drive from Sacramento to Amador City was a prolonged forty-five minutes. It was much longer than our trip to the hospital.

When I went into labor, Alex raced to the hospital, running every red light and breaking every speed limit. We had plenty of time. But at the midnight hour my contractions began three minutes apart, making him nervous. My physician had advised us to head over if my contractions were six minutes apart, and since that didn't happen, panic had set in.

We arrived home, and I settled in with my newborn daughter. Alex headed to work, and I welcomed the quiet. Isabella became my focus. I held her close as I rocked her back and forth in our living room. I admired her tiny feet and her small hands. I was amazed she was a redhead. It must have been from my father's side of the family. She would smile while she slept, and I wasn't sure if she was dreaming or suffering from gas.

I sat back while she slept in my arms. I closed my eyes and regressed in time.

∾

I THOUGHT OF ELVIS PRESLEY. HE HAD DIED IN AUGUST 1977. TEN YEARS had passed, and I remember how shocking it was. I was camping at Pinecrest Lake with Arthur. We had driven over to the small market for food supplies, and I had walked out on the small wooden deck and noticed a local newspaper stand. I pulled the newspaper out. The front page announced in bold letters, *"ELVIS PRESLEY DIES AT AGE 42."*

I purchased the paper and sat on the wood deck to read. He was a troubled man with fame and fortune. He grew up in the projects; he was made fun of at school, and he was told numerous times he could not sing. He never gave up on his dream though, and he never settled. He married the love of his life, even though that didn't work. He surely had secrets too, dark secrets. His known status became his nightmare, and he died too young, leaving behind a beautiful daughter.

∾

"DAUGHTER," I SAID TO MYSELF. MY EYES FOCUSING ON ISABELLA AS SHE rested in my arms. I was filled with a new love. It was an unconditional love, and a love that would carry me through my entire life. I gently touched her nose, ran my finger down her cheek and caressed her tiny hand. She grabbed my index finger and held on tightly.

I gazed out the window framed in ornate molding and admired the beauty that Alex maintained in our yard. His ancestors from years past left their footprints as you meandered through the wooded property.

The native foliage surrounding the home, along with their luscious scents, intensified during the seasons of each individual bloom. There were succulent honeysuckle shrubs and the delicate white flowers of the Bridal Veil that flowed like the Bridalveil Fall in Yosemite.

In the spring our first bloom, The Chinese Sacred Lily, had a golden cup nestled in the center of the small white petals. Then followed the blossoms of white and yellow daffodils, and the superior occupancy of colored tulips in reds, yellows, and pinks. The appetizing apricot scent of the oleander bush made its appearance, and lastly the petrichor aroma of my favorites–the purple and yellow Iris.

We had a weeping willow tree which provided shade in the summer and graced our landscape in the winter. Alex hated our pink flowering Tamarix that wanted to suffocate our beautiful yellow Lady Banks that gave off the aroma of violets. There were orchards of citrus smelling English walnut trees, flowering scents of the plum and Bartlett trees, and the delectable hint of coconut and pear beneath the skins of the Neanderthal fruit of the Quince tree.

Our home was built by Alex's maternal great-great-grandfather in the early 1800s. The home sat on a small hill overlooking the homestead. An ancient, monumental Live Oak tree gave way to the smoky savor after the light showers of fall. The brave carpenter who built this home was a miner that worked in the Plymouth mine during the goldrush. He and his wife passed the home down to his son and wife, and they passed it down to their granddaughter Alma (my new mother-in-law). She sold it to Alex and me once we were married.

It wasn't long before Isabella was referred to as Bella. With her fiery copper red hair, big brown eyes, and commanding presence, she was the one in charge. Much like the Dogwoods, flowering near a small corner of the property with their pungent fragrance, Bella was all of that and more. She warmed my heart along with the beautiful Lilacs. I held her close and drew in her own scent. There was the hint of vanilla and the abundance of rose. As I let out my breath, I cooed her name, *"Bella."*

LIAISON

*S*ofia, Luiza, and I parted ways two weeks before our wedding day. It was difficult when they boarded a jet to Sao Paulo from the San Francisco International Airport. I wanted to join them and soar away over the runway of fears; never to make another mistake. I waved a gentle goodbye as I watched the aircraft taxi to runway 28R. The day was cool, and the month of September was nearing to an end. Fall had shown the familiar signs of change. The Bay Area was cast in shades of gray while clouds intermittently brushed against the skyline of Oakland.

I drove the closely related road to Amador County, and the ticky-tacky homes from my past swirled across that skyline, fading to a memory. I sat mesmerized by the broken white lines that separated me from oncoming traffic. I had slipped into my robotic state. My mind capturing a glimpse, here and there of black Porsches and the eyes of Andre. Having Sofia and Luiza in my home, and conversing in the romantic language of Portuguese, brought on the heartfelt memory of Andre. I lingered in that moment of our youthful love, and I smiled.

I had arrived at my new destination, my new home in the small quaint town of Amador City. I sat silently in our Chevy Pickup, beneath the wood beams that supported the interior roof of our three-car garage. I admired his 1938 Buick Special parked alongside me. A sense of doubt continued to probe at my subconscious. I shook my head to shed the leaves of fall and doubt. Our Benz wasn't home yet.

The brilliant shades of orange and yellow lined the streets of downtown Amador City. They had given the town a sense of quaintness. It was tiny, and the local market reminded me of the small Porter's Market in San Leandro. Faint remnants of early morning showers scurried down the gutters leading to our driveway.

I forced my steps to take me into the house. I opened the door with caution, as though I had something to fear. My eyes had scanned the kitchen countertops, the condition of the bedroom and the cleanliness of the bathroom. A feeling of despair sat like a stone in my gut. I became rigid, just like the ancient tree trunk on the weeping willow.

It was late afternoon, and the temperature was comforting. I took a seat on the grand front porch swing. I admired the hewn wood plank siding on the exterior of the home. The windows were original and still had the rope and pulley system to open and close them. I rocked back and forth, reminding me of my childhood when others sat on the swing set at Dayton Elementary. I struck a match and watched as it ignited into a magnificent flame. I sucked on my Marlboro cigarette and pondered, *Who was this man I was about to marry?*

A week passed, and I was inching closer to matrimony. Mail had arrived and a phone bill was among the many pieces of junk mail. I opened it and scrutinized the details. Our telephone bill itemized each phone call that was made. It listed the phone number along with the date and time. I could not help but notice one phone number in particular that was called numerous times. It was a toll call, and it was made to someone in Pioneer. I compared the days and times to the dates I had been in the San Francisco Bay Area, with Sofia and Luiza. They matched. I remember I had called Alex and let him know we were staying an extra day. My call was listed as "collect," and he had immediately made a call to this mysterious number. They conversed for a few brief minutes.

My mind assembled the puzzle pieces together. I imagined the owner of the phone number coming to our home that very evening. I imagined the wine glasses, the candles burning, the music by Grover Washington Jr. playing "Winelight." The bed sheets washed and the bathroom garbage emptied. The stone sank deeper into the gallows of my bowel. I felt sick, and I teared up. I knew. He was dishonest to me.

I slowly dialed the phone number, waiting while it rang on the other end of this magnificent machine. I developed a lump in my throat.

A woman answered. "Hello?" she said.

I cleared the lump, "Hello, my name is Tess Hamilton, and you are listed many times on my phone bill. I am engaged to Alessandro Caminetti, and we are about to be married in one week. Can we talk?"

There was a long silence, and then she responded, "Yes, I would like that. My name is Vicki Robust. Let's meet for lunch. How about tomorrow?"

"Perfect," I responded. "How about twelve-noon at the small café in Pioneer called Chili Cooking?"

"Sounds good," she confirmed.

I spent the evening with Alex, pretending that everything was normal. My insides were wrenching, and I tossed and turned in our bed. The darkness of the night and the absence of the moon created an unnatural atmosphere. My mind spun and questions piled up, one by one, as I calculated what I was going to say.

I dressed the following morning, wanting to look my best. I was, after all, meeting the woman who had enticed my fiancé from my embrace. I could hardly contain myself, and I gathered a sense of strength within me. *I was in charge*; I told myself. This was my platform, and I would let no one ruin my life. I needed to find the truth, and in my searching, I was hopeful Vicki would give that to me.

I made the drive to Pioneer and parked in the dirt parking area in front of the small café. A wood sign carved out the words, "Chili Cooking." It swung from chains fixed to the entrance roof line. It was a favorite for my parents, who lived just down the road. I entered and was seated in a small booth next to the front window. I nervously waited for Vicki. The large cedar pines surrounded the café. An occasional vehicle drove past on Highway 88, making its way up the mountain. Logging trucks traveling down the road applied their air brakes, making a loud hissing sound as they zoomed by. There was a large cedar mill just below Pioneer. It was the largest pencil mill in California. The entrance displayed a large pencil on each side of the road. The clock pendulum ticked back and forth on the café wall. I tapped my fingers on the table in rhythm with the clock. Suddenly, the entry door opened.

A petite, pretty woman approached me. She had long dark brown hair with large chocolate brown eyes. Her skin was fair, and she smiled while giving me a nod. She wasn't much taller than me, but she was well endowed. I flashed back to my beauty pageant and the contestants who shared her stature. My shoulders sunk down, and I stood to say hello.

"Hello," I said, and she sat down in the booth, taking the seat across from me.

"Hello, Tess," partially revealing her perfectly white teeth. It felt awkward, but I pushed my shoulders back, took a deep breath, and relaxed. We ordered our lunch, and I absolutely knew I would not be eating it. It didn't matter. I was eager to dive right in and cut to the chase.

"So, let's get to the bottom line. What is your relationship with Alessandro, and why are there so many calls on our phone bill made to you? Have you been to our home in Amador City and were you there the night I was in the Bay Area?" I proceeded. I raised my eyebrow and waited.

Vicki responded, "Yes, I was there. I remember the suitcases on the floor in the dining room. Alex said they belonged to your friends from Brazil. When I was in the bedroom, I noticed your high heel shoes on the floor next to a chair under the window. I noticed they were small, and I imagined you looked just the way you do. Alex and I have been seeing each other for a few weeks. I work at a grocery store he frequents for work, and we developed a mutual interest in each other. I found him very handsome, and he pursued me with such enthusiasm."

That sounded familiar.

I had to know, so I went for the jugular. I asked with persistence, "Are you sleeping with him? I mean, have you had sex with him? Do you love him? Does he love you? What exactly is going on between you?" I sat back and waited for her response.

She finished chewing her salad bite and answered me. "Yes, I have had sex with him. Yes, I love him, and yes, he said he was in love with me. He told me he loved you, but… he was not in love with you."

I blinked non-stop. My head spun and the airplane in my heart wanted to take off. I sat still and swallowed the words. Vicki continued eating, and I gazed at the voids fading in the distance, never forgotten.

"Thank you for your honesty," I finally said. "You enjoy your lunch. I am finished here, and I will take care of the check on my way out. It has not been a pleasure meeting you. However, I sincerely appreciate you showing up. I am getting married in one week to Alessandro, and I have so much to think about. You take care."

I paid and left the café. I drove to my parents' home at the end of Inspiration Drive. I passed the signs listing the last names of all the residents on this road. I noticed "Hamilton," and I wondered, *Will I actually take the name of Caminetti?*

I slowed to a stop in front of their cabin in the woods. Smoke circled up from the chimney in a cork-screw fashion. I walked to the steps leading down to their front door, passing the water wheel on the way. The winds aloft swiftly moved through the branches above the cabin. The air brushed past my ears, much like fresh water flowing toward the ocean. Its presence abiding.

I sat in their living room fretting over my coordinates. That was when I really needed some comfort. I needed words of advice, and I needed it from my father and mother.

And there it was, with my mother sitting next to my father's side. The words escaped, and the advice was later taken. "Marry him, Tess. You will never go without. He will always provide for you. He comes from a good family and he loves you. Always remember that when a man is given the right opportunity and finds himself in the right situation, he will always cheat. You need to forgive, forget, and move on."

He can't be serious, I thought. I needed to let that sink in.

I left in confusion and made my way down Highway 88 to Sutter Creek. Alex's parents were in New York, visiting family on the east coast. I wanted to confront Alex, but he wasn't there. He was still on the road working. I had noticed his sister Francesca's car parked in back.

She watched me as I stopped in the driveway. She soon appeared and hollered, "Hey Tess! Come on in and have a glass of wine with me!" I waved a yes gesture with my hand and turned off the engine. It was obvious that I had been crying, so I tried to clean up the mascara streaks on my face.

I walked through the back-porch entrance and relaxed in one of the lounge chairs resting inside the screened-in porch. Angelo and Alma's home was breathtaking. I let out a sigh. I wanted to be a part of this family, but at what cost? Francesca appeared with two wine glasses and a bottle of Amador County's finest. It was an extraordinary Barbera wine. This region had the perfect climate to grow its well-known aged vines. Francesca poured us each a glass. She raised it to make a toast and then noticed my red eyes.

"What's happening?" she asked. We sipped our exotic spiced wine, and I unfolded the events of my day. She quietly listened, and I could see her wheels turning in her head. She waited until I was done. I finished with my father's words of advice, and then I sat back, my head spinning.

"So, this is what I suggest," she pushed on. "You should go home and prepare a nice dinner for Alex. Everyone reacts better on a full stomach. After dinner, retreat to the living room and tell him everything you told me. Hear what he has to say. He will probably fess up to this, since he can no longer deny it. Ask him if he truly loves Vicki? If he does, then call off the wedding. If, and I repeat, if he tells you it was just a fuck, which he probably will, then tell him to never do that again, and marry him. Maybe he needed to get that out of his system, Tess. He loves you, but my brother can be senseless, and I know him. He is Italian and thinks he lives in Italy. I am not excusing his misbehavior, but you are not man and wife yet. Think about it and go home."

Her words echoed Arthur's sister telling me, "Go home, Tess," in the wee hours on a dark corner in San Leandro. I wondered how other's see things so differently than me? *Can I be that forgiving... again?*

I did as Francesca suggested. I prepared our dinner of spaghetti, salad, and French bread. Alex bounced in with the enthusiasm he always displayed. I pretended to be my usual self–happy and excited about our wedding. We conversed about his day during our meal, and I told him I had visited my parents.

We retired to the living room, and that's when I unloaded on him. I blasted him with my revelation and my lunch with Vicki. I was trying to be calm, but I turned into that turbo-bitch that lived in San Leandro; the one that had married Arthur. The rage resurfaced, and it was beyond my control to contain myself. I broke down and began sobbing, and that is when Alex began talking.

"I am sorry, Tess. Yes, I saw Vicki for a very short time. Yes, she was working in the grocery store I go to once a week. I was sewing my wild oats, and I wanted one last fuck before the wedding. It was meaningless. And she means nothing to me. Yes, I told her I loved her, but that was only because she said it first. I didn't mean it. It is you that I love, and I never wanted to hurt you. I was reckless and foolish, and I see that now. I will never do that after we are married. I will honor you and I will be faithful. You have my word, Tess. I want to marry you and I can't imagine life without you."

I retired in the guest room. I pulled the covers over my head and continue to unload every emotion I had bottled up inside me. I had a drill-sergeant marching through my head. My brain was rotating around and around. The pendulum swayed back and forth on the wall clock. I felt as my ancestors probably felt when they had an arranged marriage. I was no longer getting married for love. I was getting married for financial security, and I would become a partner in the family business. I had moved into our home and I had purchased my wedding dress, flowers, and arranged for the photographer. Plans were in place and my soon to be in-laws were bringing our wedding cake. I felt trapped, small, and stupid. I never wanted to give up on love.

I made a decision in that hour of confusion. I would not give up on us. Maybe my father was correct. Maybe, just maybe, men are incapable of keeping their 501s buttoned up. They are weak in matters of sex. "It meant nothing," he said. I could not relate to this concept, but in time I would.

EMERGENCE

*J*t was August 8, 1986, when I went into labor. It began as a simple evening–dinner with Alex, enjoying homemade tacos. It was one of our favorites. Alex loved to cook, and I never felt bad about cleaning up the kitchen. It seemed to be a team effort, and that evening wasn't any different.

I cleared the table and filled the dishpan with hot sudsy water. I was quite uncomfortable, and my due date of July 30th had passed. We used olive oil for much of our cooking, and I recall grabbing the bottle in one sweeping motion. It belonged in the revolving cupboard just below the kitchen counter's corner. I did not realize the lid was loose, and in leaning over I inadvertently spilled the entire contents on the interior shelf. It was a slimy mess, and in that moment, I stood feeling helpless. My back ached and the thought of cleaning up spilled olive oil was about as bad as falling down a ski slope that was covered in solid ice. It seemed there would be no end.

I began with a lot of paper towels. Painstakingly one by one, I cleaned up the spill. Other items, covered in oil, had to be washed in the sudsy water. My kitchen chores came together as warm air does when it hits a cold surface. I had reached my dew point. I was exhausted. Alex watched television in bed. I stood in the living room, wondering if this would be the night? My eyes moved back and forth and quickly stopped when the clock struck 10:00 pm. I felt like a whale, and I wanted to change my mind, but then I recalled the nursery and the baby clothes–all in blues and greens. I told myself I was going to have a baby boy. I wanted that so much; I had convinced myself I was having a boy.

I retreated to the bedroom and attempted to sit on the mattress edge, but could not. I had a sharp pain in my lower abdomen. I stood, moaning. I tried to sit again, and this time the pain intensified. I had Alex's attention, and he groggily asked questions–questions I could not answer. I was in too much pain. "Let's see how far apart these pains are, Tess? We need to keep track in case they are six minutes apart." Alex reiterated.

I walked back into the living room and continued walking in a circle. I moaned each time the pain began, and Alex timed the flexing of waves. They slowly rolled in, similar to the tides at the Bird Sanctuary in San Leandro. As the wave broke, it receded back out into the ocean. Three minutes apart.

Alex panicked. He immediately made his way to the shower, as I jogged around the imaginary high school track in our living room. The contractions came more intensely, and I wanted so much to recede like the waves. I wanted no part of this. Fear set in, and I knew I was committed. It was like when my father pulled back on the control wheel in his airplane; we were committed. There was no going back, and we took flight. My flight was just beginning, and the waves continued to break.

I used to joke with Alex about wanting six children. Had I kept to my wishes, we would have been halfway there. But as our life played out, we welcomed in our firstborn child. "Push, come on push, Tess!" Alex chimed in with all the nursing staff. It was 4:45 am, and I was in the last stages of labor. I looked into his chocolate brown eyes, overshadowed by his unibrow. A surgical mask covered his beard. He clasped my hand and continued to coach me.

My water did not break on its own, so when the doctor broke my water, the contractions were at their peak. They wheeled me out of the labor room and rolled me down the hall to the delivery room. "Push," the nurse told me. I recall looking up at the face of a janitor, mop in hand, as I passed by. Water was everywhere, and I got the impression a tsunami trailed behind me. I felt as though I was on display, and the notion of modesty no longer had any meaning.

I delivered Isabella at 5:07 am. It was beyond any pain I had ever felt. I chose to have a natural childbirth. Hence, I was not given anything for pain. I later realized that was not the best choice. After that last push, the doctor announced it was a girl!

I was so tired from exertion my first response was, "When are you going to circumcise him?"

The doctor stood and gave me the look. You know, like the one my sister Katie would give me. He raised the upper right side of his lip and responded, "We are not going to circumcise HER!"

I relaxed back against my pillow and chuckled... I was so sure it was a boy.

When I looked at my daughter for the first time, her small body and damp red hair were covered in blood and amniotic fluid. I motioned for the nurses to clean her up. Alex took Bella from my arms and walked over to an area where he and the nurses cleaned, measured, and weighed her. When Alex returned, her skin was pink and wrapped tightly in a matching blanket. He handed her to me. I studied her face, her eyes, her tiny mouth, and her unibrow. I looked up at Alex, and then down at her, and I knew. I was no longer empty... I was blessed.

I STOOD OUTSIDE MY HANGER DOOR, RESTING MY FINGERS ON THE DOOR'S handle. It had been a good flight, and the breeze lightly brushed my face. The memory of Bella's birth lingered as I locked the door and walked to my car.

A BLACK HOLE

*T*he sound was overwhelming. I found myself falling from the resounding truth. Light became dark and I could hear faint words. "Come back, Tess, come back." I was awakened by smelling salts. The doctor loomed over me while Alex held my hand.

It was two years after Bella was born. She had been playing in the living room with her toys and I sat alongside her. I wasn't feeling well, and I had entered my second month of pregnancy with another child.

Bella was a handful. She was walking and talking. She would hand me a toy and then insist I quickly return it. She would hug me around the neck and squeal when her daddy entered the room. I loved watching them interact. Alex held the Magnavox camcorder across his shoulder. It was my surprise for him at Christmas, just after she was born. She would sing for him and run through the house giggling.

It began with fatigue and slight bleeding. Alex insisted I see my doctor, and before long, we were on our way to Sacramento. After my arrival, I was instructed to get an ultrasound to determine the timeline of my pregnancy and to make sure all was well. Alex and I walked to the adjacent building and arrived for the procedure. I did not have an ultrasound with Bella. This was a new procedure for me.

I was instructed to lie on an examination table, and the technician applied lubricant on my belly. He then ran a wand across my abdomen and would stop from time to time, making clicking sounds. The screen was hard to read, and the technician was quiet. Within a few minutes, my doctor arrived. He reviewed the images with the technician and moved the wand around on my abdomen as well. Soon, he asked Alex to join us. The doctor informed us I was indeed pregnant, but I appeared to have a fetal sac without an embryo. He called this an anembryonic pregnancy. It was his opinion that my body was attempting to abort the pregnancy, and that would account for my bleeding. He gave us a couple of options. We could go home and allow my body to go through a miscarriage, or we could return to his office and he would perform a dilatation and curettage (D&C). It was entirely up to us.

Alex and I stared at the monitor, and then at each other. I glanced up at the doctor and asked, "What would you do?"

He responded, "I think we should head over to my office and have the D&C. That way, Tess, you can go home and rest knowing it is over. In a few months, you two can try again to have another baby."

Alex nodded.

I responded, "Ok, let's go to your office."

I was ushered into an examination room with my doctor's nurse. I climbed onto the table and looked up at the ceiling. It was white, clean, and desolate. The machine fired up, and I was quickly reminded of the pain I had experienced twice before. It was the same procedure, but now we are calling it a D&C.

As I starred at the ceiling, I thought, *How ironic? When you are choosing to stop a pregnancy, it has an ugly term. But, when one finalizes a miscarriage, it has a sterile professional term.*

The suction removed any life that may have existed within me. It entered the black hole and faded into that intergalactic void. I began to breathe heavily. I couldn't believe I was doing this again. The pain was intense, my legs quivered, and then it was over. The doctor patted my leg and said I could relax.

He called Alex into the room and explained the process. He reached into a small cup and his fingers swept through the slug he had removed from me. "As you can see, there is nothing here except blood and gunk.

And here is the sac and here...oh wait...here is the fetus!" he said in amazement.

That is when I fainted. I fell into my eternal darkness and knew I had just aborted a third pregnancy. It was more than I could bear, my body gave up and I surrendered. When I awoke, Alex's voice saying, "Come back, Tess." He clenched my hand and continued to assure me everything would be alright.

I don't recall saying any words. I kept to myself, and our drive home was voiceless. Both of us knew what had just happened, and we both knew that it had been our decision. It was another wrong decision, but we had to live with it.

"What did the doctor do with it?" I finally asked Alex.

"He just closed his palm, removed his glove and disposed of his glove in the garbage can."

I let out a sigh. I hated myself. I looked out of our front windshield as tears streamed down my cheeks and thought of Bella. I loved her even more now. I wanted to hold her. I only hoped that one day I could forgive myself, again. I prayed that God would.

It was a cool afternoon. Alex built a fire in our wood stove, and I looked in on Bella while she napped. I paid our babysitter, Allie, and sent her home. She lived in the home next to us. It was a short walk, and I felt lucky to have her so close. I settled in and relaxed by the fire.

I picked up a *Reader's Digest* and began reading. An article caught my eye. It was regarding abortions. With extreme hesitation, I read about the procedure, which was too familiar. Then it explained (in detail) the weeks of development. There was a chart showing how the embryo develops into a fetus within eight weeks. It illustrated each stage; forming a heart, the eyes, the fingerprints and their movement.

Then, I read about "The silent scream." They referenced a documentary via ultrasound showing a fetus's mouth opening at the moment it was extracted from the womb. My mind jolted to a stop. I couldn't read anymore. I did not know. No one had ever told me this. I stood and threw the *Reader's Digest* in the fire.

My thoughts moved to the conception of our universe. The universe blends three dimensions of space to one dimension of time. That makes us four dimensional. We are body, mind, and heart. And then we are spirit. I felt as though I lost my spirit that day. I became separated from my fourth dimension. It traveled near the speed of light, left suspended somewhere in the vastness of theory.

I took my three-dimensional self to Bella's room and watched her as she slept. I laid down on the floor beside her bed. I heard an album play by Cat Stevens. "If I Laugh" resonated against the walls, and I listened carefully to the lyrics. Alex appeared in the room. He took my hand and raised me to my feet.

He placed his arms around me, and then in my own sounds of silence, we walked down the hallway to our bedroom.

BIANCA

I fell into a deep depression. The reality of life sunk its way into me, much like the flood waters that sink into the lowest point on our property. Eventually, they dissipate from our view, but continue trickling down beneath earth's surface, finding a new resting place.

Bella was a new place for me, but she would not give me rest. She was vibrant, intense, and in constant motion. She was the only one who could pull me out of this without even knowing that she had that power. Bella's copper red hair and natural curls matched the color of her eyes. She had a nice olive complexion, much like her dad's. She was growing in size, as was her vocabulary. She displayed advanced dexterity and a fiery temper. I was told that was common among redheads. She would stand with her fists on her hips and demand our attention. It was comical at times, but I dared not laugh. This would send her into tears. Bella was my challenge, and Lord knows I deserved one.

We grew together, Bella and me. Alex continued following us around with his camcorder, taking it to all our family gatherings. I adored watching them play in the yard. Bella would remove all her clothes and run about free as a sparrow. Alex would run to catch her and get her dressed. But to no avail, her clothes would be off again. We became a work in process and between cooking, cleaning, canning fruits and vegetables, and bookkeeping, my fourth dimensional spirit slithered its way back into my third.

The Elderberry hedge lined the walkway edge to our porch. I hoped the myth held true. With its urine scent after a light shower, it would ward off evil. My eyes were not completely focused straight ahead. I found they shifted back and forth looking for that clue, that bit of information which would lead me to Alex's infidelity. It was there, distrust stood right in front of me. He masked himself well, but the Bella inside my heart refused to believe otherwise, so I ignored all the signs.

Alex and I started hanging out with another couple. I missed the company of James and Demi; however, Jasta was his best friend while growing up in the small town of Sutter Creek. He had married a local schoolteacher named Cheryl. They had one daughter, Lilly. We discovered a common ground between us. We doubled every Friday night. We played racquetball at a private club nearby and finished with dinner at our favorite Mexican restaurant. It was time away from children, and I came to relish our evenings out. We seemed to click, the four of us. Jasta owned and operated his father's antique furniture business. He also began taking flying lessons at our local airport. I was intrigued, and I asked questions about his flying progress each time we sat down for dinner. I was jealous, knowing flying lessons were at my wing tips, and yet they seemed completely off my radar.

Angelo and Alma would watch Bella on those nights. They seemed happy that we found one evening a week to get out. Alex was so busy with the family business. Angelo had worked so hard maintaining his family bakery. He was known in the county as "The Bread Man." When he passed down the business to Alex, Alex claimed the title.

Alex worked non-stop five days a week until I came along. I took over the bookkeeping portion, and this freed up Alex from paying bills, balancing the spreadsheets, and making routine bank deposits. I relieved him of that and without realizing it, I also freed him up to develop his interest in golf, or so he said. I became a golf widow, and that eventually ate away at our evenings out with Jasta and Cheryl.

I began feeling a change in my body again. It was the familiar change when one becomes pregnant. After a few weeks, I took another pregnancy test, and it was positive. Alex and I were expecting another child. It was different this time. I carried my child low in the abdomen area. The pregnancy warranted morning sickness, and I was not used to that. Fortunately, it didn't last long. My belly continued to grow, and Bella continued to ask questions. She would sit on my lap and rest her head against my belly and rub her hand across with a glee in her eyes. She seemed excited as she approached the age of three.

I wondered if I would have a boy this time. The desire for a son was still there, and I wanted so badly to pass on the family name. That was important in an Italian family, and it seemed I was always wanting to please others. I wanted to make sure everything was going well this time. I was scheduled for an ultrasound, and shortly thereafter, the doctor confirmed everything was normal. I was also informed by the technician that I was having a girl. Disappointment set in, and I wondered if my boy had moved into that never-ending void. We announced our expectant baby girl after the first trimester. Alex's family seemed elated, and so began my six remaining months of pregnancy.

I recalled my days at home shortly after Bella was born. We would lie in the twin bed in her nursery. I loved placing her on my bare chest while lying on my back. She would sleep listening to my heart. We were still connected and the bond between us was indestructible. I couldn't imagine having that much love for another child. I hoped I would, yet Bella's smile and demanding presence created doubt. She consumed me, and every moment was a deep breath. I took her in much like my need for oxygen. I heard the wind chimes softly sing just outside Bella's window. It was the sound of *God's* whisper that all would be right. I imagined the silhouette of the Oak trees, rolling hills, and the twilight sky. They soothed me, as did His presence.

Having an extended family helped me in so many ways. Alex's family taught me the most fundamental values. I learned to cook. The Caminetti garden's grew vegetables and spices. The orchards of fruit-bearing trees grew in perfect formation. There was plenty to go around. Alex taught me how to braid garlic, and every year we entered our braids in the Amador County fair. We received many blue ribbons (although Alex took credit for them), and I looked forward to the entries each year.

My mother entered her crochet items. She made bedspreads, table-cloths, and doilies. Each year she also received blue ribbons. Our home was decorated with her talents and our kitchen table was decorated with his, including the bouquets of flowers from our yard. I emersed myself in this new lifestyle. I cherished being a wife and mother. I had purpose for the first time in my life, and although my husband continued with his black out absenteeism, I was determined to focus on family. I closed my eyes when it came to Alex, but I opened them when it came to Bella.

Bella and I would sit on the front porch swing and watch as Alex rode his riding lawn mower. The smell of fresh cut grass filled us with calm as we rocked back and forth. My belly was larger, and the arrival of our second daughter was only four weeks away. I was having difficulty lifting Bella and carrying her on my hip. She wanted my arms around her seemingly every moment. I worried that she would not be able to share that comfort with her sister.

As I continued to rock Bella on the swing, my mind drifted to James and Demi. They had married years before and welcomed in two boys. I laughed at the remark James had made to me when Bella was born. They were visiting us, and he boasted, "Hey Tess, if you want a boy, I can tell you how to get one. Just hang your head out the window and yell... Jimmy!" He laughed, and I chuckled at this memory. I missed those two. Demi had such a love for life, and I never, ever, heard her speak negatively about anyone. They were right up there with my idea of a perfect couple, along with my sister Angie and her husband Mel.

A few days went by and I received a sickening phone call. It was my sister Katie. I stood lifeless, numb, and shocked. My dear friend Demi had drowned. Her oldest son found her. He was only seven and tried his best to pull her out of their bathtub. It was a large tub with jacuzzi jets. James was away at the time, and her son had sense enough to call 911. The emergency medical team could not revive her. She was pronounced dead on September 4, 1989.

My phone rang endlessly the next day. Many friends and family had called to see if I was okay. I wasn't. I gravely mourned, and I couldn't stop crying. It was unbelievable, and I couldn't imagine how those two little boys dealt with this. Her youngest was only two years old. James was probably a mess and feeling unimaginatively horrible for not being there. It was not his fault. My heart remained heavy that night before I went to bed. I kissed Bella goodnight and tucked her in. Alex was already fast asleep, and I laid quietly next to him. The flood gates had sluggishly closed, and my tears reflected sadness from a gentle slow-moving creek. The full moon cast a shadow across Alex's face.

I placed my palms on my belly and slowly moved them back and forth, trying to comfort the child that waited inside me. She moved abruptly and stretched. I felt a fist punch my lower uterus. I glanced at the clock alongside our bed and it read 1:00 am. I had been awake so long and so consumed with Demi, that time quickly disseminated through space.

I could trace her little hand on my belly, and I wondered if she was disturbed by my grief. The pain intensified, and suddenly I realized I had gone into labor. The waves moved in, and I shook Alex to wake him. "It's time," I said. "I think my labor has started."

Alex rose and looked at the clock. "You are early, Tess. Let's time the contractions before we jump to any conclusions," he reiterated.

The wave reseeded, and then it rose again. Two minutes had passed, and I moved to the living room to begin my walk around the track. Two minutes continued and Alex called our babysitter, Allie. She was there in a few minutes, sleepy eyed, but willing to watch over Bella as we left for the hospital.

Alex pulled the Benz out of the garage and waited in the car with the engine running. A contraction hit me, just as I was midway down the stairs from our back porch. I stopped to breathe through it. Allie had been watching and ran to me, offering her assistance down to the car. "I can't believe Alex isn't helping you," she whispered.

"It's ok," I whispered back. "If he was here, then I wouldn't have you!" and then she smiled. We made the slow walk out to the car.

My water did not break on its own (again), and the delivery nurse tried to break it while waiting for my doctor to arrive. She pushed her fist inside of me, and I immediately kicked her in the chest. The bitch in me told her to stop and get out of my room. However, my words were much harsher. I realized soon that the nursing staff did not give me pain medicine in retaliation for my behavior. When my doctor arrived, he broke my water. I had another natural delivery.

I delivered Bianca Caminetti on September 6, 1989, at 9:44 am. I heard the doctor say, "I see a hand!" I had sensed my body was ripping in half. Bianca's tiny fist was first to arrive, then her arm. Her shoulders had to be rotated along with her head during my last push.

I held my newborn and counted her toes, her fingers, and admired her blonde hair. She had a small round nose and blue eyes. She looked like me with fair skin. I marveled at her beauty, and then I paused and thought of Demi. My tears flowed, and I struggled with the loss of a dear friend and the birth of my new child. *How does one separate the two?* I looked up at Alex and asked, "Demi is gone, and Bianca is here. I don't know how to process this."

He stroked my head and tried to comfort me. "Just rest, Tess, you will get through this."

"Please bring Bella here this evening. I want Bella here with us. I want her to meet her new sister," I said.

I was transported to my private room. I moved Bianca carefully to her basinet next to my bed. I was in pain and needed to sit on an invalid ring cushion. I had many stitches, and I had cracked my tail bone during labor and delivery. I let out a deep sigh and thought of Demi. I would miss her funeral and that troubled me. I took out a pen and paper from my nightstand and wrote. I wrote a letter to James and told him how very sorry I was. I wished so much I could be at her funeral. I wanted to say goodbye.

I closed my eyes again, reopened them. But this time it would be for Bella and Bianca. I was blessed a second time.

YELLOW BANANA IN THE SKY

*R*umor had it that Jasta and Cheryl had split up. They were getting a divorce, and skuttle-butt around town was that Cheryl caught Jasta cheating with another local woman. Both Alex and I refused to believe the gossip chain. At that time, Alex became more focused on his golf score and less interested in racquet ball. On Friday nights I entertained Bella and Bianca, waiting for the return of their father.

Alex's high school graduation class was hosting a fifteen-year class reunion. We decided to make a weekend of it and headed out of town. Alex and I checked into our hotel room. It was a nice hotel, with a jacuzzi bathtub. I cringed at the thought. The event was held in a small banquet room. Alex and I ordered a cocktail and took our assigned seats for dinner. No sooner than I took my first sip, Alex nudged me. In walked Jasta with the other woman, and rumors were confirmed. The other woman was pretty, young, and popular in the community. Her name was Julia. How quaint, I thought. Jasta and Julia, what a lovely couple. I was resentful of her. Neither Alex nor I approached them, and we didn't speak to them that evening. I had become fond of Cheryl, and Julia seemed wrong to me. Jasta must have worn a pair of 501s as well.

Those buttons were always popping open. Another validation of my father's advice.

Eventually Jasta and Julia were married. Alex suggested we double on Friday nights again, so he and Jasta could return to racquet ball. There was that word *forgiveness* hanging above me. It seemed tides came in and tides receded. My level of forgiveness was constantly being tried. Even for the acts of others. With a hesitant heart, I agreed to go.

Bianca was an angel sent from heaven. She would go to sleep as soon as I put her down. She would curl up into a ball, her bottom stretched high in the air, and fall asleep. I was so thankful for her easiness. This gave me time to tend to Bella. Bella always needed time in the rocking chair, or a story before bed. Sometimes she refused to allow Alex to put her to bed. I would be in Bianca's nursery feeding her, and I could hear Bella screaming at her father, "I want my Mommy to put me to bed, not you!" I would feel bad and wanted so much to comfort her, but I was busy with Bianca. I needed to share my time, and I understood Bella wasn't used to this. Alex would tell her, "Mommy is busy, so I am putting you to bed!" Bella would cry even louder.

Bianca rarely cried. Occasionally, she may have woken up from a bad dream or a bout of indigestion. I would bounce out of bed and retrieve her from her crib. I would rock her back to sleep. I could soothe Bianca, but I think she was the one who soothed me. She was balanced and her spirit was calm. They were the perfect opposites, Bella and Bianca. The doctor said they were from two different molds. I would agree with this, both equally different and equally perfect. Bella carried the Caminetti genes with a hint of Hamilton. Bianca carried the Hamilton genes with a hint of Caminetti.

As my two bundles of joy grew in size, Alex and I grew apart. We had moved away from the idea of hanging out with Jasta and Julia. In turn, he embraced his golf swing and not my embrace. I felt alone and my purpose, while fulfilling with children, was dissipating. I was missing something, and I searched for answers. I started walking around our small town, in the evenings after the kids were in bed. Alex would retire early, and I would put on my Adidas running shoes and head out. I would think about flying and how much I missed it. I wasn't traveling abroad anymore, and my father had sold his airplane years ago.

One afternoon, I drove to Angelo and Alma's home with the children. I asked if they would watch the girls for a few hours. I drove to the local airport and sat in my car drooling over the rows of small airplanes. I noticed a sign above an office door. It was made of wood and a small airplane and "*Calaveras/Amador Flying Club*" was carved into it. I slowly exited my car and walked over to the flying club. I opened the unlocked entry door and discovered an older man sitting on a couch.

The club was set up like a living room with a large chalkboard on one wall. I noticed a hallway with the front fabric of shirts hanging on the wall. They were dated and signed by pilots from their first solo flight. It was tradition for an instructor to rip off the student pilot's shirt upon their return. The older gentleman stood and said, "Hello, can I help you?" He had gray hair and a pencil mustache. The gleam in his eyes and the smile was so familiar.

"Yes. I am interested in learning how to fly," I responded.

"Oh, really? Why is that?" he quizzed me.

"My father is a pilot. I flew with him for countless hours, and I have always had a desire to fly."

"Ok, I would love to teach you. Let me introduce myself. My name is James Douglass, but you can call me Jim. I am a retired captain from Hughes Airwest. I was based in Oakland, California. Why don't you sit down and let's talk? I would love to hear more about you. Do you have time?" he asked.

"Yes, of course I do." I responded with enthusiasm.

I began sharing my past life with Captain Douglass. We discovered we both had owned Karmann Ghias. He had purchased a black 1954 Ghia for his late wife. He was a breath of fresh air, and the more we talked, the more comfortable I became. Hours passed, and when I realized the time, I stood to go. "I need to get back to my children," I said.

"Ok, but let's set up your discovery flight. How about tomorrow? Let's say around 8:00 AM?" he asked. "Oh, but before you go, I have a homework assignment for you. How many sections are in a banana?"

I went blank. I had no idea! "Well, I am not entirely sure, Jim. I will research that and let you know. I'll give you a call and confirm tomorrow morning as well. I need to discuss this with my husband. It was a pleasure meeting you!" I responded.

I went out to my car and started up the engine. I moved the gearshift to reverse and backed out of my parking space. I paused for a moment and flashed back to the Los Angeles terminal in 1974. I recalled Captain Angel helping me through customs and finding a flight to San Francisco. He had that gleam in his eyes and the pencil mustache.

"Nah," I told myself. "That's impossible." As I moved the transmission into drive, I couldn't help but wonder... what did a banana have to do with flying?

MAGGIE MAY

I made the usual drive to Amador City. Bella and Bianca were seated perfectly in the back seat. I noticed in my rear-view mirror Bella tending to Bianca. It brought a smile to my face. I tuned in the FM station, and Rod Stewart was singing his hit "Maggie May." My mind always drifted when I heard this song. It swiftly sent me back to 1972 and a party at my friend Meggie's home.

It was a typical Saturday night. My friend Yvette called and announced a party at Meggie's. Yvette picked me up in her Ford Mustang and I was looking forward to seeing our sweet girlfriend. We headed to Meggie's, and the drive was short. She lived in the Manor and just on the other side of town. Music blasted from her garage. It was separated from the main house and had its own entrance on the adjacent street. Meggie's parents had converted the garage into a recording studio. She had an older brother who played in a band. Cars lined the street, and Yvette and I had to find a place to park further down the block. Both of us had an ear-to-ear grin as we walked to the garage. All I could hear was Rod Stewart. I smiled at the thought, *Meggie was playing "Maggie May."*

As we entered through the gate, the familiar smell of pot lingered in the air. Faces emerged in the backyard and I motioned to Yvette for a smoke. She and I lit our Marlboro cigarettes and then made our grand entrance into the garage. It was smoky, and the black lights gave my white pants an iridescent glow.

I was short, but Meggie was even shorter. She had long dark brown hair, big brown eyes, and a big smile. I walked up behind her and tapped her on the shoulder. "Hey there, girlfriend!" I said as she spun around. "Did Rod Stewart write this song about you?" I hollered with a big grin. Then I looked down. Meggie had been away from high school for a few months. I heard she had some medical issues. It was apparent now, she did indeed. Meggie was somewhere between six and seven months pregnant.

"What the? You are expecting, Meggie! When, how, who knew? Does Tim know?" I spilled out question after question. Meggie just kept smiling and then hollered in my ear.

"I wrote and told Tim, but I'm not sure if he knows yet. Mail sent to Vietnam is slow, and I haven't heard from him. I am really happy about this, Tess. I am going to be a Mom, and I am completely okay with this. I hope it's a boy and I hope he is healthy." Meggie had a gleam in her eyes. She was glowing, but not from the black lights. It was the glow a woman gets when she is with child. I held out my arms and gave her a big hug.

"I am going to throw you a baby shower! Let's plan on getting together for that. I am very happy for you, Meggie!" I hollered in her ear. Meggie meandered through the crowd of people in the sound studio and I noticed Derk standing in the corner. He smiled at me. I lifted my upper right lip and walked away. I was over him—way over. I found Yvette, and we gathered around people, then I started dancing. I started thinking about a baby shower, and the thought of a baby at our age was frightening. We were all seventeen, I thought. Maybe some of us older, and some younger.

Seventeen, I pondered. Wow, a baby...

BELLA STARTED CRYING FROM THE BACK SEAT OF THE CAR. I GLANCED IN the mirror at her and asked, "What's the matter, Bella?" Bella hollered out,

"I don't like that song, Mommy!" I smiled and changed the channel. Bella settled down, and I glanced at Bianca asleep in her infant car seat. She was still so tiny.

I tried to hold on to those thoughts, but I drifted back to Meggie.

YVETTE AND I PLANNED THE BABY SHOWER, AND I SENT OUT THE invitations for a Saturday afternoon. I was hoping Meggie hadn't gotten wind of it. I made it a surprise for her. My classmates, Lexie, Susan, and Darcie arrived and help set up the living room. I had taken up a collection, and we bought Meggie a stroller. We filled the stroller with gifts, as guests arrived, and waited for Meggie. Time ticked by and still no Meggie. I called her on the phone. "What are you doing, Meggie? I thought you were coming over today and hanging out with me?"

Meggie sounded sleepy. "Oh my gosh, Tess. I forgot all about it. Maybe I can come over another day?" she asked.

"No, I really wanted to see you. I can come over and pick you up?" I insisted.

Meggie stood her ground. "I am exhausted, Tess; I will pass today."

I stood baffled, and realized I had to spoil the surprise, "Ok, Meggie. I am having a surprise baby shower for you today. Everyone is here, except you. Now will you come over?"

I SWUNG INTO THE DRIVEWAY AND PUSHED THE GARAGE DOOR OPENER. I had been in deep thought when we seemed to suddenly arrive home. I was a long way from the Bay Area, and yet it seemed like only yesterday that I was that teenager. Funny how songs will move you from here to

there in a split second. Bella giggled as we exited the car. I reached in and unstrapped Bianca. She smiled when I removed her from the car seat. The three of us made our way up the steps and into our home; Bella held my hand and Bianca was on my opposite hip. I unlocked the door and Bella ran in. She was happy to be home, and I was happy about the possibility of my first flight. I had waited for this moment my entire life.

"Hey Bella?" I hollered. "You want to share a snack? I have to peel a banana!"

CAPTAIN ANGEL

*M*eggie lost her baby boy shortly after he was born. She named him Timmy. Something had gone wrong. I wasn't sure of the reason. It wasn't until much later in life, she would share that with me. I had grieved her loss back in 1972. Afterwards, when she returned to school, she was very depressed. No one said anything. No one would.

Now it was April 1992, and I continued to hang on to that memory. After getting both of my daughters to sleep for the night, I laid in bed and tried to make sense of it. I could not. Why do some of us make wrong decisions that follow with regret, while others make the right decisions that follow with pain and confusion? We have choices in our lives, and God has given us free will. Yet, we roll the dice, and we don't always win. Demi rolled through my mind. My miscarriage rolled through. My two unwanted pregnancies rolled through. I was riddled with guilt and anxiety. Their silent scream became mine.

Suddenly I felt a presence. Alex stood in the bedroom doorway with just his bath towel draped around his waist. I could smell him. It was clean, sensual and warm. I raised my naked body out of bed and embraced him. I buried my head in his chest. His skin was soft as I ran my hands down his back. His touch was gentle as he caressed the small of my back and drew me in. Tears trickled down my face. I loved this man, yet in my heart I sensed he would never have my trust. He stared at me with that look in his eyes. The look of lust. I was exhausted, but Alex was never truly exhausted; not even after a hard day of work.

He lowered me onto our bed. He was a passionate man, had strong intensity, and was well scripted. He knew just how to please me, but he seemed to take more pleasure in the mere act of lovemaking. My anxiety was masked by his self-absorbed quest. My tears went unnoticed, as did my pain. He had grown to be complacent. I wondered if maybe, just maybe, somewhere deep in his heart he really did love me.

Alex fell into a deep sleep from his sexual gratification. It was the only time I could lay close to him, snuggle into his shoulder and fall asleep with my head resting on his chest. Eventually, he would turn over and I would stare at his backside. I would rotate onto my back and contemplate. From just beyond our bedroom window, the nocturnal nightjar birds sang, and the streetlamp glowed in such a way I could see the sign of a cross. I would squint my eyes and it would become brighter and then I knew. There was hope.

I woke early with the girls. I recalled Bella and I having our snack yesterday. It was the banana homework. I chuckled as I smashed a banana into Bianca's oatmeal. Bella preferred hers with brown sugar. I couldn't wait to tell Captain Douglass. I had been given the "go-ahead" by Alex to take my discovery flight today. I had butterflies in my tummy, as Bella would say. It was a beautiful day with a cool temperature. Allie had agreed to come over and watch the girls. They loved Allie. When she arrived, they both became very excited. Bella ran to her arms and Allie picked her up. Bianca sat with her cereal spoon, banging it on her highchair tray. She would squeal when she saw Allie. I smiled too, because that was always a good sign. I knew they were in good hands.

My anxious drive to the local airport reminded me of watching seagulls. I soared around the turns, descended through the dips and accelerated up the hills. I was so excited to be flying again. The anticipation was nerve-racking. I pulled up in front of the flying club and shut down my car engine. I hesitated to get out. I glanced at the American flag hanging limp on the flagpole. "No wind," I whispered, "It's perfect."

Captain Douglass was waiting on the same couch, sitting in the same place I had left him the day before. "Hello, Tess! How are you doing today? Are you ready for your big day?" Jim questioned.

"Oh yes, Captain. I am ready, and I am really looking forward to this flight. I researched how many sections are in a banana." I responded.

"Ok, Tess. Tell me. How many sections are in a banana?" he grinned.

"Three! And, to my knowledge, it is the only tri-segmented fruit in the world!" I said with confidence. Captain smiled and there was that gleam in his eyes again. His gray hair brushed across his ears and his gray pencil mustache played havoc on me.

"Very good, Tess. That is correct." He confirmed.

I waited for further explanation, but he just continued smiling. "Ok, Captain. I have to ask. What does a banana have to do with flying?" I quizzed.

He paused and then he said, "Not a God-damn thing, Tess. Everyone should know how many sections are in a banana, and call me Jim." We both laughed, and I knew I was right where I was supposed to be, listening to Captain Douglass explain the principals of flight.

We walked out to the airport tarmac and toward the club Cessna 152 airplane. It was orange and white with a bright orange stripe across the wheel fairings. Jim referred to them as wheel spats. I chuckled at the idea. I asked non-stop questions while Jim walked around the aircraft. I stop to listen as he explained the importance of the preflight inspection. We looked at the plane in its entirety. I stepped up onto the side cowling and removed the fuel tank cap, which was on top of each wing. "Stick your finger in, Tess. Make sure you can feel the fuel. Always check that, Tess, and if you can see in, take a look. You always want to verify the fuel levels. Ensure they are topped-off and no tampering has occurred. Mistakes are best found on the ground, not in the air. Now, replace the fuel cap, step back down, and check the other tank on the opposite side."

Jim explained the aircraft fuel tester and demonstrated how to use it. Located under each wing, he drained a small amount of fuel from the fuel tank sump drain into the tester. We checked for dirt or water. The fuel was clear except for a small bubble that sank to the bottom. Jim pointed out that water weighs 8.34 pounds per gallon and 100LL (or

Avgas) weighs 6.02 pounds per gallon. What appeared to be a small bubble was water, and so it sank. He emptied the tester and drained more fuel into it until it was clear.

"Why would water be in the fuel tank?" I asked.

"Condensation, Tess. This aircraft is tied down outside and when temperature changes, such as it does at night, condensation occurs. It's normal, Tess. No need to be alarmed," he said with a grin.

I realized there was so much to learn, and this was only the beginning.

We completed our pre-flight inspection and jumped into the airplane. Jim asked that I sit in the left seat as he took the right. We went through our pre-flight checklist from the glove-box. There were identical controls on both the left and right side. That way one can fly an airplane from either seat. Then, he asked me to start the engine. Jim talked me through the entire process while he kept his feet on the brake pedals. I followed his instructions. "Let's taxi around the airport first, Tess, so you can get a feel of the rudder pedals and the throttle. I want you to feel the aircraft's yaw and how much pressure you need when engaging the throttle."

Jim and I moved about the airport's row of hangers, and I found the taxi maneuver to be familiar and smooth. "Tess, taxi over to the runway. Let's go flying!" Jim hollered. It was loud in the airplane, and so we both put on our headsets. I followed the taxiway broken lines until we reached the end of runway 19. Jim had me observe while he did a run-up with the engine, checking the magnetos. He turned 360 degrees on the ground (a full circle), checking for any incoming or outgoing aircraft. Since we did not have a tower, it was up to us to clear the area for take-off.

"Ok, Tess. Time to go flying!" Jim motioned to proceed onto the runway. I taxied onto runway 19 and stopped. I gently pushed in the throttle, released the brakes by sliding my feet from the top of the rudder pedals to the bottom. I powered down the runway and gently applied back pressure to the control wheel. Jim tapped on the airspeed indicator and motioned for me to apply more back pressure. The airplane lifted off, and the engine torque caused the nose to move left. "Apply right rudder, Tess, get that nose straight!" Jim instructed.

I applied more pressure to the right rudder and straightened out the nose. We continued our climb, and Jim asked me to look out the back window. I turned to look and noticed we were not on a straight-out departure. We had veered off to our left, and I saw how easy it was for the engine torque to rotate the airplane.

We climbed to 3,500 feet and leveled off. Jim talked me through different flight configurations. We flew over fields in the San Joaquin Valley, and I carefully guided the plane through ground reference maneuvers (which means I was flying in rectangular patterns). I was having difficulty maintaining my altitude, while changing headings, so Jim spit on his index finger, then leaned over toward the windshield. He pressed his finger against the windshield and left a fingerprint level with the horizon. He instructed me to turn 360 degrees and keep that print on the horizon. I was not to exceed an angle of 10 degrees and maintain my current airspeed. I followed his orders and executed a right turn, dipping my right-wing no more than 10 degrees, my hand on the throttle to maintain airspeed, and my eyes glancing at the fingerprint on my horizon. I rolled out of my turn at 360 degrees. My palms were sweating, and my mouth was dry.

"Great, Tess, now make a left turn the same way!" Jim exclaimed. After rolling out of my left turn Jim commanded, "Let me take over and I will execute a full stall!"

My mind raced. I hated roller coaster rides, and I had the distinct feeling I was about to experience one. Jim gently pulled back on the control wheel. The plane climbed slowly while he continued back pressure until the plane could no longer sustain flight. The stall horn blew, the plane shuddered, our lift was broken, and then the nose dropped. We fell out of the sky like a bird who just propelled himself off the top of a building. I was suddenly looking at the ground. Jim allowed the plane to fall, reduced throttle to idle, and gently applied back pressure on the control wheel. We slowly pulled out of the dive, easing the throttle in, and flew again. He leveled out the plane and looked over at me. I was white, my eyes wide open, then I smiled.

"How did you like that, Tess?" he asked.

"I hated it," I replied.

We headed back to the airport. My one-hour discovery flight literally flew by. It was time to make my first landing. "I will talk you through this, Tess. Just follow my instructions and you will do fine." Jim voiced.

I entered the landing pattern for runway 19. The radio was quiet and thank goodness there wasn't any air traffic. I reduced the engine power and deployed the flaps; first 10 degrees on our left downwind approach. Then 20 degrees when we were parallel to the runway heading 19, and then 30 degrees when we turned left base. Jim continued to talk me through the landing as we turned left base to final approach. "Keep your eyes on the third line, Tess, and point the airplane's nose there. Hold it there." As we closed in on the runways third line, he said, "Now, forget about the third line and look at the far end of the runway, allow it to slowly come up in the windshield and watch your airspeed indicator." I did exactly as he said, and I slowly descended.

I applied back pressure on the control wheel and allowed the runway to rise in the windshield. Then I pulled back as hard as I could, as I heard Jim saying, "More, more, more." The slight hum of the stall horn could be heard. The soft squeak of the wheels settled on the runway, and the gradual downward motion of the nose wheel softly touched the ground. I slid my feet tips on the brakes and gently applied pressure. We slowed to the taxiway and stopped. My knees were knocking together, and my smile was from ear to ear.

Jim looked at me and said, "Great landing, Tess. That is probably the best landing you will ever make!" and then he grinned.

I was so emotional over my first flight; I could not taxi the plane. Jim took over, and we taxied to our designated tie-down area and stopped. I observed the shutdown procedure and followed through with lock down and tie down. We chalked the wheels and proceeded to the flying club.

As we entered the club, and took a seat on the couch, a thought came to mind. I hesitantly asked Jim, "In 1974, were you at the Los Angeles Airport? Did you help a young girl from customs over to Western

Airlines in order for her to catch a flight to San Francisco Airport?" Jim's eyes looked me over, very slowly and carefully. He then removed his eyeglasses, pulled a handkerchief from his pocket, and cleaned his eyeglass lenses. He put them back on and let out a long breath, looked up at me again and smiled. "Well, I'll be dammed. That was you?"

WORLD WAR II

*B*ella and Bianca were both baptized at birth in the same Catholic church as their father. While suspended over the marble baptismal font, Bella cried as the priest poured holy water over her head. Bianca slightly flinched during her christening. Father John had agreed to baptize our daughters, both times, and both times with the promise we would marry in the church.

It was always my intention and hope, but since we had not and never would, we were unmarried according to the laws of Catholicism. I watched the holy water gently trickle over Bella's red hair over the beautiful marble font. Her cries broke the solemn silence within the cathedral walls. Bianca, lying still and placid. Their ancestors must have looked on with pride–there was a story linked to the church's cold and monumental stature.

ANGELO CAMINETTI WAS ENLISTED IN THE UNITED STATES AIR FORCE, just after graduating from Amador High School. He was their star quarterback, lean, tall, and extremely handsome. He shadowed his older brother, hoping to one day be as brave as he. Angelo became an aviator-navigator in the Air Force. He had become part of their special operation forces, navigating for a cockpit crew. It was during World War II when everything changed for Angelo.

On August 17, 1944, the United States had sent 1,973 aircraft over Yugoslavia, dropping over 3,000 tons of bombs. Germans occupied Sarajevo, and the Italians had quit the war in 1943. King Peter II of Yugoslavia had fled in 1941 from a small airport in Niksic. It was to become one of those situations, being in the wrong place at the wrong time.

On August 21, 1944, during a return flight from a bombing mission, Angelo and his crew were shot down over Sarajevo. He, along with those who were able, parachuted out. Their pilot did not make it. Angelo landed in a tree and dangled there for hours. It was by sheer luck that a local man spotted the crew. He had tracked them as they fell out of the fallen plane. He could hear Angelo crying out for help. Angelo was hoping the man approaching was not an enemy soldier. This man, known as Drago, came to his rescue.

Drago rounded up the remaining seven Americans and hid them in his home, taking a monumental risk from the Germans discovering them. He and his wife spent weeks nursing them back to health. They became friends, he and Drago. They made their plans to leave during the night, and hike over the rugged terrain. The temperature was frigid at an elevation of 8,839 feet.

They departed on foot from the outskirts of Sarajevo and back-packed east over the Dinaric Alps, then southwest to Niksic, Montenegro. Niksic was occupied by British Armed Forces and was 200 miles away. It was a good four to five weeks by foot. Drago led the Americans to their first checkpoint, only to be passed off to other locals led by General Dragoljub Mihailovich. General Mihailovich led the Chetnik movement, fighting against the Germans, and another movement led by Josip Broz Tito to force a communistic government in Yugoslavia. Tito claimed victory with his partisans in May 1945.

They took cover during the day and traveled by night. It was grueling for them, and I can only imagine the anxiety they must have felt, along with the desire to make it safely home. The villagers who helped to aid and hide them, took an enormous risk at being captured themselves. Some entire villages were burned, and locals were killed as punishment for harboring Americans. General Mihailovich went to great lengths to protect our soldiers. He considered us an ally since we were fighting the Germans. He was fighting to save Yugoslavia from the Communist and Nazi invasion. The downed soldiers came to respect and admire this man. Our government finally recognized him some years later, after his execution on July 17, 1946, for high treason. Our government presented his daughter with a *Legion of Merit* award.

Angelo's crew had arrived in Niksic-Montenegro, at that small airport on October 19, 1944. Angelo said goodbye to the Chetniks, under the cover of the surrounding trees. The American crew were loaded into a C-47 transport. They departed on the 700-foot one grass runway, making their sweeping turn (just clearing the treetops) and over the surrounding mountains. Angelo looked down at his bare feet– his worn boots were left behind for those who had none. He had tears in his eyes as he headed to the neutral territory of Italy. His heart, so thankful for the kindness of Drago and his comrades. It was then, on October 20, 1944, when Angelo sent his mother and father a telegram. He was alive and on his way home. He was flown from Italy back to the United States.

Angelo's mother did not know if her son was dead or alive. She had only been informed, months earlier, that he was missing in action. She had prayed for the safe return of her son and promised the Holy Church a gift, if her prayers were answered. When she received news of his safety, she purchased a Carrara Marble baptismal font from Italy. It was shipped to America and placed in the small church where she had spent each day praying.

AS I WATCHED BELLA AND THEN BIANCA BEING BAPTIZED OVER THAT VERY font, I pondered the realization. That certain event would never have taken place if it had not been for the bravery of those soldiers of World

War II, General Mihailovich of the Chetnik movement, Drago, and the power of prayer.

His Majesty, King Peter II, was the last king of Yugoslavia, and perhaps he would not have fled on that small *one grass runway* in Niksic, Montenegro either.

Without those sacrifices, Alex would not have been born or baptized in that church, suspended over that same marble font. I would not have loved him, and my two daughters would be part of the void that vanishes in the universe somewhere, fused between the conception of space and time.

BEYOND THE CLOUDS

$\mathcal{T}$he winds aloft can be very different from those on the ground. When I am flying, there is a sense of freedom that no one can pull me away from–not by the arm or words. There is no one there to intimidate or shame me. I would look down on the earth and notice the small specs of movement. Some were cars slowly making their turns around the roadways. They appeared so small and unimportant. Then there was the slight ripple in the waters, the brown smoke from a nearby lumber mill, or the bending branches of the autumn oak trees, aiding me in determining which direction the wind was moving.

I learned to fly through the efforts of my instructor. He taught me to imagine the air flow just as you would the flow of water. It moves up the windward side of the mountain and spills over the leeward side. It rushes over the leading edge of the wing, faster than the trailing edge, creating the Bernoulli's Principal, or lift.

Air, unlike water, does not contain as many moisture molecules so we cannot see it. However, when it becomes saturated enough in the right temperature, it becomes visible in the form of clouds, rain, hail, and even snow. When I flew over dry fields, I could anticipate air moving upward as thermals, when heat rises. If I crossed over a body of water, or a moist green pasture, I could expect the air to be moving down.

As my aircraft penetrated this invisible water, it would respond and react to these conditions. It could be bumpy, as in a bumpy road, my father would say. I may experience a sudden lift, or an unexpected down draft. The airplane spoke to me, and I listened. I would make necessary corrections and adjust accordingly. My eyes became the eyes of a bird, my fingertips became the tips of a bird's wings, and my senses were permeated by Captain Douglass.

When he wasn't flying with me, he spoke to me. His words locked into my inner core. He became my guiding light, and I flourished. I was his student, his small and delicate bird about to leave his nest.

Jim and I set out for another lesson and after 20 hours of flight time, he decided it was time. As we taxied out to the local runway 19, I was instructed to stop the plane. Jim opened his door and climbed out. He leaned in and said, "It's time for your first solo flight. I will be on the ground watching. Stay in the pattern and make three full-stop take-off and landings. When you are finished, taxi in. Don't worry, Babe. You are ready and I wouldn't send you alone if I didn't think so."

I cringed and begged him not to leave me. There I was, remembering my father leaving me on the ground and flying away without me. Only this time, I was leaving Jim. I swallowed, licked my lips, looked straight ahead, and taxied forward. I executed the usual run-up and cleared the area for inbound air traffic. I announced my departure over the radio. I taxied into position and released my brakes. With my right hand, I gently pushed in the throttle and powered down the runway. My left hand gently applied back pressure on the control wheel, and the nose lifted. In an instant, the plane ascended, and I glanced to my right as the right control wheel moved simultaneously. The rudder pedals on the right moved up and down as well. I was alone and without the added weight of my instructor; the plane lifted off faster than I expected, and an emptiness entered my cockpit. It was up to me to land, and there was no one by my side.

That was when he first spoke to me, my Captain Douglass. In my mind, I could hear his commands–his tapping on the airspeed indicator. I watched the ground as I turned left at the correct altitude. "Now, Tess," I heard, and I turned left to fly downwind of the parallel runway.

I reduced power and lowered the wing flaps to 10 degrees. "Watch your speed, Tess," he would say. I adjusted my airspeed and once I was parallel with the opposite end of the runway, I reached for the wing flaps and increased to 20 degrees. I made another left turn, turning left base, and increased the wing flaps to 30 degrees. I then executed a final left turn to line up with the runway 19. "You are lined up perfectly, Tess. Forget everything around you and focus on the runway!" he would instruct.

I recall moving back and forth in my seat and wiping the sweat from my palms against my pant legs. My knees shook. I focused on the third line, and then at the right moment, my eyes moved to the opposite end of the runway. I watched as it slowly moved up in my windshield. I gently reduced power and applied more back pressure. As I crossed the numbers 19, I could hear the slight hum of the stall horn and the gentle squeak of the tires on the runway. The nose wheel touched down as I held the control wheel back.

Jim stood off to the side of the taxiway with a thumbs up. I completed this maneuver two more times. Each time, I would remember his instructions, his gestures, and I would comply. My nervousness kept me alive. I was alert because of it, and my own life depended on it. I was the bird that autumn morning in 1992. I was living out the dreams from my days in Oakland, California, as I sat on that park bench at the marina. It was only a dream then, and now I was flying, and I had two beautiful daughters and a loving husband who supported me in this.

After completing my three landings, I taxied to the tie-down area. Jim was waiting with his big smile. I shut down the aircraft engine and ran through my checklist. I locked the control wheel and got out. I chalked the tires, and that is when Jim approached me.

"Great job, Babe! I would tear off your shirt, but that would not be appropriate. You can bring this one in at your next lesson, and we can write on it and display it alongside the others in the flying club hallway!" He shook my hand, "I will refuel the airplane, let's relax in the clubhouse before you leave. We can discuss your solo flight."

Captain Angel Douglass had flown in World War II as a transport pilot. He would ferry Martin B-10 bombers to France during the night over the Atlantic Ocean. Radio communications were silenced. His only reference were the stars to navigate by; celestial navigation intrigued me. *Those were true pilots*, I thought. Now that I had experienced landing an airplane, the thought of landing on a 700-foot grass runway (at night) was indeed a *home run*.

That was when I really flew. Jim had pushed me out of his nest, except I was still training on a 3,401-foot asphalt runway. We became close, and he always called me Babe. I cherished our relationship. When I excitingly told Jim, he was the grandfather I never had; he balked. "I'm not that old... maybe I could be your father," he said with a wink.

RUMBLE

*A*lex and I had been married for eight years. We were planning our anniversary trip to Napa-Sonoma, California. I had read about the hot-air balloon flights, and I had talked Alex into going for the weekend. We left early in the morning while our girls lay sleeping. Grandma Alma arrived early as well. The children would be in her care while we were away. I left my curlers in my hair, knowing it would be a few hours' drive.

Alex loaded our luggage into the Benz and waited in the car. I recall bouncing out of the house, anticipating a fabulous time in Napa. It was October, and the fall leaves radiated yellow and gold tones. We headed out on Highway 16 toward Highway 50, and then we were going to get onto Highway 80. I was talking nonstop about my excitement to ride in a balloon. I glanced at the Highway 80 sign as we passed by it and headed north onto Highway 5 instead. "Hey Alex, you missed the turn!" I insisted.

"Don't worry, Tess. We are not going to Napa. It was a surprise, but now I have to tell you. We are headed to the Sacramento Airport. I planned a trip to Victoria, British Columbia. We are staying at the Empress Hotel," he beamed.

My mouth dropped open, and then I smiled. "Oh shoot, I have my hair rollers in!" I said, immediately pulling them out.

I was a bit disappointed about the hot-air balloon trip, but I had always dreamed of staying at the Empress Hotel. It was so British, and that meant we would be able to have tea-time at high-noon. I chuckled at the thought. Alex had given much thought to this surprise. He was trying to bring a bit of romance back into our marriage. Children have a way of changing things, and parenting brings a new set of dynamics.

We boarded our American Airlines 707, inbound to Seattle, Washington. Alex made a reservation to stay one night in Seattle at the wharf. It reminded me of San Francisco, but with a different energy. The surrounding estuarine of the Puget Sound was breathtaking. It connects to an inlet of the Pacific Ocean and the Salish Sea. We nestled down in a hotel right on the dock near Pike Place Market. I recalled hours spent on Fisherman's Wharf in San Francisco, tearing apart sourdough bread, sharing a beer, and savoring a shrimp cocktail. I squinted my eyes as a boat with a large mast passed by the hotel room window. My thoughts interrupted as its horn blew. This was our night, and the satisfaction of our earlier seafood dinner, wine and dancing seemingly trumped that of Fisherman's Wharf.

Alex and I seemed to be compatible in every way. We gravitated to the same food, the same music, and the same movies. We both enjoyed travel and entertaining new adventures. He was delicate in so many ways, but he was always a man in charge. I accepted him and his wandering eyes. I excused his ghost like behavior, and I wanted to believe I was more important than anyone else. He could wine and dine me in a way that ferried Elio back into my thoughts. I tried to erase him, but he lingered there. His memory seized a small part of my heart, incapable of being erased.

In the morning, we enjoyed Starbucks coffee along with fresh warm cinnamon rolls. We strolled over to the Seattle Ferry Terminal and checked in for our excursion. I was relieved when I had packed my wool coat and gloves. The temperature was cold in October. We boarded the San Juan Clipper Ferry, traveling through the Puget Sound with scenic views of the San Juan Islands. It had a feel of being in a foreign country.

The small islands gave way to small airports, rows of large yachts, and quaint restaurants. Beautiful homes were tucked inland, and residents had to travel by boat or air to come and go. I reminisced about my father's dreams of living on a boat, sailing at sea, or flying in his small Cessna, landing on Friday Harbor. A flock of seagulls soared overhead, and I took in a deep breath. It was moist salty air I had grown to love.

Victoria rests on the southern end of Vancouver Island. We arrived at the Inner Harbour entrance. It was exquisite. I marveled at the antique lampposts, each adorned with a hanging flowerpot. Flowers hung in clusters of pink, yellow, and red. The Empress Hotel sat majestically amongst double-decker busses passing over the cobblestone streets. The French Renaissance historical brick hotel was covered in green ivy. It seemed we had stepped off our boat and entered England. The influence was pungent and the colors vibrant. I was in awe, and Alex was pleased. He felt as though he had hit a *home run*. *"Home Run,"* I thought to myself; a day I would never forget.

It was October 17, 1989–eleven days after Bianca was born. I had retreated to her nursery and Bianca and I fit comfortably in the rocking chair. Bianca took to nursing easily, but I had not realized she was allergic to lactose. We struggled with her cramping stomach and each time she started crying, I assumed she was hungry. The more I fed her, the more she cried. I was frustrated and so we had rocked back and forth for hours.

Bella and Alex were in the living room getting comfortable in front of the T.V. for the 86th edition of the World Series. My home team, the Oakland A's were facing off with the San Francisco Giants. It was a huge event and the first battle-of-the-bay World Series since 1956. It was Game 3 and the A's were leading by two.

Alex had made his usual quesadillas, chips, and salsa. Our Sony Trinitron's sound system was wired to Alex's Klipsch La Scala speakers. We were all tuned in, waiting in anticipation of the game start.

I felt a slight rumble as I rocked back and forth. It seemed out of the ordinary, and then within seconds, the television sportscaster's colleague, Al Michaels, announced an earthquake had shaken the stadium. It was 5:04 pm and Alex bolted into Bianca's nursery. "Tess, an earthquake has hit the San Francisco Bay Area! We lost coverage on the T.V."

All I heard was, "We're having an earth..."

I was lost for words and Alex just stood there, his eyes wide open, staring at me. My eyes shifted back and forth and my mind rushed with thoughts of confusion. That was my childhood stomping grounds, and I had many family members and friends in that area. We waited to hear something, anything about the quake.

The T.V. reception resumed with a green ABC sports screen until technical difficulties could be resolved. I am quite certain we waited along with hundreds of other sports fans who were home glued to their television sets. Audio was recovered first, and we could hear the fans at Candlestick Park Stadium screaming and rushing about in the confusion. Al Michael's voice was faint and shaky as he spoke, "Well folks, that's the greatest open in the history of television, bar none!"

Needless to say, the game was delayed as patrons scurried to exit the stadium. Concrete fell from seats above; chaos and panic were seen by news media covering the earthquake. Santa Cruz Mountains, just south of San Francisco, was closest to the shock. The Loma Prieta earthquake had a magnitude of 6.9 and considered a maximum intensity of IX (violent) in the Central Coast of California. Fires broke out in San Francisco, buildings collapsed in Oakland, and landslides occurred in summit areas of the Santa Cruz Mountains.

Hours passed and then the broadcast came of an all too familiar freeway collapsing. The Cypress Street Viaduct (in Oakland) had always given me the feeling of claustrophobia, and I recalled the evening my co-workers and I drove to see the production of *Annie*. Traffic moved toward the city on the lower level, while traffic traveling away from the city used the upper level.

The concrete on the upper level seemed as though it was right above the top of our car. The undulations gave a sense of being in a boat while passing beneath a bridge and over the waves in the ocean. It had a span of 1.6 miles. I hated it then, and I hated it when the cameras zoomed in on the devastating aftermath. Vehicles were crushed and passengers trapped.

We watched as a woman being interviewed explained in detail, the image from her rear-view mirror. She sped up, trying to avoid the falling concrete while each section tumbled down behind her to the lower level. When it fell, it was as though someone had tapped the first of many dominos. Her vehicle had rocked back and forth, and when she was clear of the double-decker freeway, she pulled over–shaken and sobbing. She had narrowly escaped death, but was devastated for those who had not.

This freeway connected to the San Francisco Bay Bridge, and the footage of its damage was unsettling. There were sections of the bridge's upper deck that had collapsed, and vehicles hung in the road with shears. The sky had a stillness that lingered among the clouds. The seagulls rested silently on the suspended cables, watching as the tide rose. Alex and I watched as more and more coverage unfolded on T.V. We were lucky. We were not affected by its quake, but for those who were, I felt nothing but sorrow.

The Series continued ten days later, but not without an emptiness that penetrated the hearts of the fans. The Oakland A's swept the Series at Game 4. The typical celebration of champagne had been cancelled. It was the team's effort to show respect for those lives that were lost. Thousands of people traveled through the viaduct, commuting to and from work, and because of the Series, they were at the game or home watching it. It could have been so much worse. Oakland A's batter, Ricky Henderson, began game four with a home run and after that, the momentum ramped up.

"*Home Run*," I whispered. I smiled at Alex upon exiting the San Juan Ferry. He was obviously pleased with himself, and I was humbled. Canada was breathtaking, and as is life, we carried on.

VISITORS AT NIGHT

I grew to love Alex deeply. That is–as deeply as one can with full pockets. I tucked myself in the *happily ever after mode*. I wanted so much to believe this was it. I wanted Alex, Bella, and Bianca to be my family forever and without interruptions. Life isn't always that kind. I looked the other way too often. It was only a matter of time when my internal clock would stop–just as the pendulum on my father's Cuckoo-clock would stop when it ran out of chain.

Alex was charming in so many ways, but he dropped into the Twilight Zone more and more. I had always hoped my deepest fears were just that–fears from my past. My memory of the days with Arthur grew dimmer and dimmer, and had faded completely into the darkness, I suddenly peered through a small opening much like a telescope. I imagined a full moon surrounded by stars, but it became obscured by the thought of Alex and another woman. My telescope had become my kaleidoscope, with little pieces tumbling all around and on top of each other.

I compared myself to a white bird that landed upon a barren autumn tree branch just outside my window's view. At times a long disappointment set in, and I realized during her solo flight she had chosen the wrong tree limb to rest on. It would sway in the chilly winds. She would have to hang on tight.

Bella was enrolled in the Montessori pre-school, just down the street from our home. She excelled in her studies. She was four and soaked up reading like a sponge. She was smart, and the teachers would comment on her artistic abilities. Her red hair complimented her intense personality. Bella was my brilliant light bulb, and with each day of education she lit up brighter. She was a stickler for punctuality and not easily forgiving.

Bianca and I arrived to pick Bella up after her pre-school class. When we entered the school, Bella was the last pupil waiting. She was furious and with her hands resting on her hips, she announced, "You are late!"

I responded, "No, Bella, we are last, but we are not late."

She marched out ahead of us and to the car. Her teacher looked surprised and said, "Well, I have never seen this Bella before!"

I responded, "Let me introduce you. This is the Bella I live with!" and we both laughed.

Bella broke into tears, "Mommy, please never be late again. I don't like being last!" I noticed Bella was seemingly more frightened than mad. I tried to comfort her and reassure her I would never abandon her. Bella preferred being first, and that was how she forged through life. As she grew older, she was always on the top of the honor lists, and her grades rarely dropped below an A.

Not long after her sister, Bianca began pre-school when she was four. Bianca was my social butterfly. She was the student who made friends easily, and before I knew it, I would have other children at our home visiting or spending the night. She was also artistic, but preferred outdoor activities, like riding her bicycle or playing on the swing-sets with other kids her age.

I watched them grow in very different directions. Each contained a mixture of fine ingredients, and each one punched from a different press. It became a boxing match at times. When we traveled in the car, Bianca complained that Bella was picking on her. "Make her stop!" Bianca would say. I would glance in the rear-view mirror and Bella would laugh while Bianca would cry. It was frustrating, and I finally told Bianca, "One day, you will have to stand up to your sister. You can't allow her to pick on you, and I can't always be there to settle things for you."

Well, it wasn't too long afterward we were in the grocery store buying groceries for the week. I was at the checkout stand, writing a check when everyone in line, the cashier and myself heard a loud commotion. I looked up and there was Bianca throwing lefts and rights, punching Bella. Bella stood two feet higher, but Bianca was dominating her. Bella was wailing. I looked at the cashier and said, "I don't know them."

That was the last time Bella picked on Bianca. I marched two crying children out to the car. While we drove back to our home, I watched a small airplane overhead. I imagined myself flying and yearning for another lesson. It was a Friday, and I wondered if Alex would show up for dinner. It was "his" day, and each Friday he would do something he enjoyed. It was usually golfing. He had become very engrossed in his *alone* time.

We arrived at home, and I prepared a simple meal for the three of us. We settled into a usual evening, and I ran the bath. Our large claw-foot bathtub gave the girls plenty of room to splash around and wash in. It was so different from my bath experience in Idaho, sharing the tub with three sisters and four inches of water. I relished the time with my girls. I was grateful my daughters would never experience what I had. I watched over them with a protective eagle eye.

When they dried off, each waited as I would cradle them in their tightly wrapped bath towels. Bianca loved the La-La-Lu song from Lady and the Tramp. Bella would sing along. I would read a bedtime story before tucking them into bed. It was our ritual each night; it was our special time.

That evening, after all was quiet, I waited for Alex to come home and I thought I heard a slight knock on our back door. I carefully opened the door, but no one was there. It was my imagination, and a reminder of when someone was actually standing there.

IT HAPPENED DURING OUR FIRST YEAR OF MARRIAGE. ALEX WAS OUT LATE, at a meeting with the Italian Benevolent Society. They met once a month, and he was usually late getting home on those nights.

I had retired early and was watching T.V. in bed. I heard a soft knock on our back door. For a second, I thought maybe Alex had forgotten his key. I put on my robe and went to the door. I opened it and was face to face with another woman. She was pretty, small framed, and surprised to see me at the door.

"Oh, I am sorry. I thought this was Alex Caminetti's home?" she asked.

"Yes, it is. He should be home soon. Would you like to come in and we can wait for him?" I asked.

She just stood there looking at me with a dumbfounded expression. "No, that's ok. I'm so sorry. I should not have come over." She seemed very nervous.

"Whom shall I say was looking for him?" I asked.

"My name is Nanette; I haven't seen him in a very long time. Just tell him I said hello" she responded.

"I will, and by the way my name is Tess," I said with a raised eyebrow.

I closed the door and went back to bed. I waited for Alex. When he arrived, I blew up. He denied any knowledge of her and claimed he had no idea why she stopped by. I am certain she had been there before, otherwise how would she know to come to our back door. Only our close friends and family used the back door.

THOSE DAMN 501 JEANS AND THOSE BUTTONS. LEVI STRAUSS SHOULD have advertised those jeans as, "Button fly, quick release." My thoughts then moved to zippers, which led to zip cords, which led to buttons, and I imagined a B-24 flying over Yugoslavia while the tail gunner pressed the buttons on his machine gun.

"Abandon ship! Abandon ship!" the pilot called out over the intercom, announcing when it was evident there was no alternative. His voice was followed by the bailout bell. Where was my bailout button to push?

What the hell was I doing with Alex? I imagined myself jumping out of the plane, just like Angelo did.

But then, I thought of those two little girls fast asleep. I wasn't the only one that would jump, it would have to be the three of us.

The shadow of that white bird, clinging to that barren branch, was now nestled alongside two small blue birds. As they swayed in the gusty winds, they hung on tightly. The white bird wasn't alone anymore.

STAR SWEEPER

"*Benvenuto!*" Alex exclaimed with a smile as we made ourselves comfortable on the lawns of Butchart Gardens; one of Canada's national historical sites. The afternoon sun had set, and darkness from the warm evening air had settled just beyond the Italian gardens. Music filled the air from many speakers hidden within the surrounding foliage. We had spread our jackets on the lawn, and the sound of Disney's, "When You Wish Upon A Star" projected from the speakers. The aerial firework display began. The twinkling stars sparkled beyond the burst of each pyrotechnic device, showering the sky in brilliant hues of red, yellow, blue, purple, and silver. It was beyond any display I had ever seen. My eyes watered and my mind drifted and there I was, in the blink of a pyrotechnic star, reflecting on another starry night.

BELLA AND BIANCA EACH HAD A RAGGEDY-ANN DOLL THAT MY MOTHER had made for them. Bianca was not as attached to hers as was Bella. Bella carried her doll everywhere. She was tattered and torn, and Raggie (as Bella called her) needed to be refurbished. We had been watching

Disney's *Pinocchio* before bed, and I suggested we send a wish to the Blue Fairy and ask that Raggie be made new again. Bella was elated with the idea, and so we began reciting, "Star light, star bright, first star I see tonight. I wish I may, I wish I might, have the wish I wish tonight. Please make my Raggie new again?" Bella asked. I kissed her goodnight and assured her the Blue Fairy would help.

Months earlier, my mother had sewn a new Raggedy-Ann doll for Bella. I had been hiding it, hoping to replace the worn out, mangled face, one armed, one legged Raggie. As Bella lay fast asleep, I quietly slipped the old Raggie from underneath her arm and replaced it with the new version. I then placed the old one in a brown paper bag and tucked it away in the event this did not go well. My heart wasn't sure about the swap, but I was hopeful Bella would accept her.

The next morning, just as the sun was rising, I heard Bella let out a cry. I went to her room and there she sat, staring at the new doll. She was howling terribly. "That's not my Raggie! That's not my Raggie! My Raggie had black eyes, this one has white and black. My Raggie had brown eyebrows and brown lashes, this one has black!" she blurted out.

"Calm down, Bella. This is the new Raggie. The Blue Fairy has made her brand new for you!" I reassured her, but she wasn't buying it. She wanted her old Raggie back. I suggested we could make another wish at bedtime and ask the Blue Fairy to make her old again. Bella agreed and set Raggie on the bed. She would not touch her all day, and she waited anxiously for nighttime to fall.

We had our bedtime story, and once again we recited, "Star light, star bright, first star I see tonight. I wish I may, I wish I might, have the wish I wish tonight. Please make Raggie old again!" Bella requested. I smiled and gave her a kiss goodnight.

I passed by Bianca's room as she lay fast asleep. She was more gratified singing "La-La-Lu" from Lady and the Tramp than getting mixed up with that Blue Fairy scenario. She clung to her blanket and a small blue stuffed elephant she had named Ellie. They were so different.

During the night, I once again exchanged the Raggedy-Anne dolls, and hoped we could figure out another way for Bella to accept the new one. Come morning, Bella ran to our bedroom with her old doll. She was elated to have her back. "I don't like Raggie new!" she reaffirmed. She was so intuitive and meticulous. Her brain was always firing and soaking up detail.

I phoned my mother and asked if she could change the new Raggie to the same color thread as the old one. She agreed, so we set out our plan. I drove both girls to my parent's home, their cabin in the woods, for a customary visit. Bella waltzed in with Raggie under her arm to greet my parents. Bianca and I followed behind. Bella showed Grandma her doll and shared her story of the Blue Fairy. I slipped the brown paper bag, containing the new doll, into my parents' bedroom. Grandma suggested to Bella that she could make Raggie new again, because she was a Rag-doll nurse. She would have to keep Raggie for a few days, and after giving her special medicine, Raggie would be all better. To my amazement, Bella agreed.

It was the longest few days when my mother phoned with the news of Raggie. She was mended and ready for Bella. I drew in a long breath and crossed my fingers. We made the drive to Pioneer, and when Bella entered my parents' home, she welcomed Raggie into her open arms. She studied her face, turned her over and examined her clothes, her feet and then drew in her smell. We all waited and watched until she said, "Raggie is new again, and she smells good too!" We all laughed, and Bianca walked over and kissed Raggie on the nose. It worked! I could finally give the old Raggie a much-needed cremation.

I waited a month before doing so.

One evening, after all were fast asleep, Alex and I placed the brown bag with old Raggie into the wood stove. For a second, I thought I heard a sound that reminded me of the Wicked Witch of the West in *The Wizard of Oz*. "Oh, I'm melting, what a world, what a world!" as she fell into a heap of water. Then I laughed at the notion. Margaret Hamilton played the Wicked Witch of the West. I wondered if she used the nickname *Tess*, as well.

THE LOUD BANG OF THE FINAL FINALE FIREWORK DISPLAY JOLTED ME OUT of my deep thoughts. I glanced over at Alex and smiled. Butchart Gardens were beyond my expectations and the moment was magical. Just like Disney, Mr. and Mrs. Robert Butchart had a dream. What started out as a limestone depository became a garden of enchantment. Despite my disappointment for the hot-air balloon ride that did not happen, I was captivated by this universal beauty.

I wondered with all my heart, if the Blue Fairy would grant me a wish. As we exited Butchart Gardens, I stopped at the bronze cast statue of a wild boar, otherwise known as the Porcellino (Italian piglet). It was a replica from Pietro Tacca's boar in Florence, Italy. Tradition has it, if you rub its nose, it will bring you luck. I paused to rub the infamous nose, and then I made my own wish. "Star light, star bright, first star I see tonight. I wish I may, I wish I might, have the wish, I wish tonight," I whispered.

We spent three days in Canada. As we rode through the cobblestone streets on a double-decker bus, I thought about my wish. I wished we would live... *Happily Ever After*, just like a Disney cartoon.

THE MUPPETS

J kept searching for a checkpoint when life seemed easier, like the memory of Samuel and I exploring and engulfed in Yosemite's embrace. It was magical and free from constraints. It seemed like a lifetime ago.

It was July 16, 1993, that I searched for a checkpoint on the ground. Behind me, I left a vast land, lakes, and the shadows of park benches.

I had departed from my local airport, navigating my first solo cross-country flight. I had spent countless hours methodically plotting my course; marking my sectional map at each landmark, checkpoint, estimated flight time, and fuel consumption. I glanced down at the Mokelumne River below and noticed the direction of wind as it rippled across white rapids, bending the treetops that lined its sandy edge.

The river's mouth connected to the Sacramento-San Joaquin Delta. For a moment, I visualized Elio and I boating on the Delta. I sunk into that memory, recapturing each moment detail by detail. I lingered in its comfort and the ground below moved past me, much like the ski boat rushing through the estuary. It took my breath away, then I suddenly captured the view ahead of me. Yosemite National Park was dusted with a bit of snow at its 8,846-foot elevation at Half Dome. I had flown from

Jackson-Westover Field Airport, to Mariposa-Yosemite Airport, from there to Oakdale Airport, and return to Westover Field.

It was a tricky runway at Mariposa. It was surrounded by a horse-shoe of mountain ranges. Its length is 3,305 feet by 60 feet wide; it dips in the center, making the landing even more challenging. My home base runway rose in the center, which prevents one from seeing the opposite end of the runway from on the ground. In either scenario, the runway is not level and the touchdown point matters. If I shoot too far down the runway, the runway heaves, either dropping or rising beneath me. The unnerving sensation makes the ground seem to move up and down rather than the plane.

I recalled the area from a dual training flight with Captain Douglass. The winds rolled over the mountain tops and spill into the canyon. "Pay attention to the windsock, Tess!" Captain would instruct. It was usually pivoting left to right, up and down, as the wind swirled down the leeward side of the mountain. It was never a good sign when a wind-sock behaved that way. I could anticipate constant corrections on my controls to steady and ease the airplane onto the asphalt.

It was no different during my first solo, cross-country flight. I was instructed to land at each airport and get my logbook signed. This was proof that I actually landed at the airports designated for training. I approached Mariposa-Yosemite with the same nervousness as before. It was intimidating to see it present itself as I made a sweeping left turn around the base of the mountain. I announced my approach on the open transmission and prepared for landing. The air traffic was clear, and it seemed I was the only plane in sight.

Captain Douglass's reminders rested upon my left shoulder; his voice whispered in my ear. I entered the landing pattern with the recommended airspeed, mechanically moving my hand to lower the wing flaps and throttling back to slow the plane. My eyes were focused on runway 26, and then I gently turned left base, applying full flaps. I analyzed the runway, focused on the third line, and precisely turned to my final approach. The winds sharply pushed my right-wing tip upward, and I moved my control wheel to force it down. I crabbed into the wind; my aircraft's nose slightly turned right. "Right rudder," I told myself.

Wind gusts pushed me upward as I nosed the plane down. *I am the white bird;* I told myself. I fought to control my landing, the runway rising fast in my windshield. I pulled back on the throttle and slowed the plane while pushing the nose down. I drifted across the third line as the runway dropped beneath me. I struggled, fighting to get the plane to settle. For a split second, I glanced at the windsock, pivoting back and forth mid-runway. The runway rose, and I touched down, braking heavily. I then slowed to the far end of the runway with my knees shaking. I had almost aborted my landing, but I had only seconds to decide, and I had chosen to own it.

I taxied to the tie-down area for transients. A voice on the radio instructed me as I positioned my ship to park. I followed my checklist procedures and shut down the engine. I unstrapped my seat belt and locked my control wheel. It was calm on the ground. I exited the plane, chocked the wheels and tied down the wings and tail. I leaned into the plane, pulled out my logbook and gathered up my purse and jacket. I looked around at this beautiful airport and the surrounding mountains. I inhaled the fresh smell of pine. I smiled at the thought of completing my first leg.

In front of the airport office, two white-haired men sat in large wooden rocking chairs on the front porch. "Hello," I said, gesturing with a nod.

"Well, hello there to you!" they both responded in unison.

I was suddenly thrust into a review session. I could do nothing but stand and listen as the men rocked and critiqued my landing as though I wasn't there. My head jerked from left to right with each comment. It reminded me of the two old men, Statler and Waldorf, who sat in the balcony on *The Muppet Show*. I grinned while listening and observing their arms flail about and their wooden rocking chairs flapping back and forth.

They finally looked at me and one of them began, "You came in high, and you needed to slip the airplane."

Then the other man countered, "She did, didn't you see her slip? She was slipping that bird real hard, but then she drifted down the runway!"

The other guy responded, "Yes... she drifted a bit, but then she thunked it, dead center on the runway! She commanded that landing."

Then the other man agreed, "Yes, she sure did. It's a tricky runway, and she landed despite the gusting winds today."

I finally spoke up and asked if someone was in the office who could sign my logbook. I revealed I was a student, and this was my first solo cross-country. I needed an entry to verify I landed here.

They looked at each other and then back at me, "You're a student pilot?"

I nodded and asked, "I am headed to Oakdale Airport for my next landing, and would that runway be as tricky as this one?"

"Oh hell," they both boasted. "If you can land here, like that? You can land anywhere!" and then they stood and shook my hand. We had a friendly laugh, but inside I was jumping over the moon. That was the greatest compliment anyone had ever given me.

I entered the small airport office and approached a woman sitting at a desk surrounded by radios, photos of aviators, and navigation charts. She stood and welcomed me to Mariposa-Yosemite airport. I handed her my pilot logbook and asked her to sign and acknowledge my point of arrival. She and I spoke about my landing, and I inquired about the two men outside. She said they were local pilots who flew in World War II. They enjoyed spending their days watching planes take-off and land. She smirked, "You had a couple of good spectators. I am certain they gave you their honest assessment of your landing. I watched it as well, through the window. I have seen many airplanes abort their approach and go around for a second or third attempt. For a moment, I wondered if you would. However, you touched down and inside, I was applauding you!" She shook my hand and initialed my logbook.

I walked out to the front porch and thanked the gallant men for their compliments. "Have a good flight to Oakdale. Don't be nervous! That runway is flat as a board and there aren't any mountains around it. You'll be fine!"

I smiled. As I walked back to my airplane, I listened to the familiar crunch under my feet from pine needles. I could almost taste the air and the memories of Yosemite.

I prepared for my second leg and taxied to runway 26. I followed my run-up procedure and made my 360-degree ground sweep, looking for any air traffic. The radio was quiet, nothing in the sky for miles, and I announced my departure. The windsock pivoted, and I took in a deep breath as I taxied into position and gently pushed in the throttle, pulling back gently on my control wheel and releasing my brakes. I rocked back and forth on the rudder pedals, and while increasing speed to full throttle, I lifted off the runway. The winds lightened up as I ascended the mountain range and focused on the San Joaquin Valley ahead. I smirked at the thought of my two Muppets, then my body tingled at the thought of Samuel lying in that tent.

I soared over the land below and transformed from a blue-eyed white panther, to a blue-eyed white bird. I graduated from the bench at San Leandro's Marina to the cockpit of a small airplane. It wasn't the big jet airliner I had fantasized about, but it was close. I looked down at the small ranches and the circling smoke rising from their chimneys, and I whispered, "I am here, high above, and I am looking down upon you."

FROM TYPEWRITERS TO ENGINES

*T*he Demorest Bicycle and Sewing Machine Company was founded in 1845. They became the innovators, setting up production in a small factory nestled in Williamsport, Pennsylvania. The factory expanded production and by the 1900s they were not only pumping out New York Bicycles, and sewing machines, but added typewriters, opera chairs, and many other inventions to their production. In 1929, they introduced the first Lycoming piston air-cooled aircraft engine. Williamsport was seated in Lycoming County, hence the name Lycoming Engine.

Captain Douglass owned a 1971 Cessna-152, which housed a Lycoming 0-235 piston air-cooled engine. When he expressed an interest in selling it, I jumped at the opportunity. I discussed this at length with Alex. He and I decided it would be a good investment, and I could continue my flight training in an airplane that we owned. Alex insisted I rent a hangar at the airport so it would be protected from the outside elements.

Within a few weeks, I was training in my very own airplane. I would hang out at the airport more and more, washing and waxing the plane. My daughters eagerly would join me, and they would sit inside the airplane and pretend they were flying. At the time, it felt like a good idea to immerse myself in aviation. I studied every moment and enrolled myself in ground school courses, studying for the Federal Aviation Administration (FAA) written exam. Alex was enthusiastic about the idea of flying to numerous destination golf courses. I was admittedly engrossed in achieving a passing score.

When I was flying, I could apply the practical classroom training to the actual skills in the cockpit. They went hand in hand for me. I was a visual person, and even though I understood the materials when I sat behind a desk, the relative principals of flight were a reality when I was engaged in many maneuvers. Captain became my wingman and had it not been for his continual encouragement and reinforcing demeanor, I may have given up. The deeper I sunk into aviation, the more difficult and challenging it became.

"I'm not a quitter," rang in my head. The words of President Nixon carried through, and from there I recalled my life in the San Francisco Bay Area. My sewing classes, along with my auto mechanic course, helped me a great deal in life to come. The power train portion of my ground school courses reminded me of my high school mechanical course. I used to work on my 1954 Karmann Ghia engine, which was very similar to the 0-235 air-cooled Lycoming engine in my Cessna-152 airplane. The training of my youth became my wisdom in my future.

It was all linked, and looking into the memory of puffy white clouds I realized I was supposed to be right where I sat, in the left seat of my airplane.

"I've got it, Babe!" Captain Douglass announced. We were on a training flight, and the puffy clouds were directly ahead at twelve o'clock. I glanced at him, as he licked his mouth, noting that his eyes were narrowing in on the clouds. "Now, don't ever do this, Tess! You are not instrument rated, and you can only fly with clear visibility. Just follow through with me, I want you to experience flying through a cloud." He grinned as we approached, closer and closer. I waited in anticipation as white veils began passing over the wings. A thick fog rolled over the nose, and the inevitable zero visibility cloud encased the airplane. We had entered the "soup" as aviators call it.

My inner ear did not agree with my eyes. Suddenly, the brain could not determine which way was up or down. I had the sensation we entered a steep bank, but we had not. I glanced at the instrument panel and noted the airplane was straight and level. I looked out of the cockpit windshield and again; it felt as though we entered a steep bank to the left. The spurious sound of another aircraft's engine hummed behind us.

"Trust the instruments, Tess!" Captain tapped the artificial horizon, or attitude indicator instrument.

We popped out of the cloud to a clear blue sky. It gave me a sense of removing a blind fold from ones' eyes, a balanced symmetry of sorts. We both had an ear-to-ear grin. I looked around and noted all was clear. Captain let out a long and slow breath, "Ok, Tess. Take me home!" He released the controls, and I took over.

We flew back to Jackson Westover Field. I made the usual inbound pattern entry over the small town of Jackson. I announced our approach over the open frequency and ran through my landing checklist. The acronym was G.U.M.P.S., which stood for: Gas (Fuel on the proper tank, fuel pump on as required, positive fuel pressure), Undercarriage (landing gear down), Mixture (fuel mixture set for landing), Propeller (prop set), and Seat belts (fasten and secure).

As I entered the landing pattern, making my left downwind approach, I glanced over at Captain Douglass. His eyes were closed, and he was slumped forward. I hollered, "Jim, are you ok?"

He jerked up to a sitting position and looked at me with his eyeglasses dangling on his nose tip and said, "Jesus Christ, Tess! You almost gave me a heart attack!"

"We are about to land, and I thought you had died. Don't you want to follow through with me?"

"Not really, Babe. You are doing great. Just don't wake me up like that again!" he said with a wink.

I made my left base to final approach. I focused on the third line, and when my position was low enough, I shifted my eyes to the end of the runway. The gentle sound of the stall horn announced the runway, and it slowly rose in my windshield. I touched down and gently allowed the nose wheel to touch last. "Perfect landing, now don't bring those wing flaps up until you are completely off the runway!" Captain reiterated. I slowly turned off the runway and stopped just beyond the taxiway marking. I raised the wing flaps and then proceeded to my hanger.

Afterwards we discussed our flight, and a short time later, a tired Captain Douglass departed from the airport. I was exhausted and ready to pick up Bella and Bianca at daycare. I closed up the hanger and jumped into my car.

Driving down the road felt strange; I had the same sensation as *sea-legs*. I was navigating on the ground and I found it peculiar. I recalled the wind chimes gently singing on the porch outside Bella's bedroom window. I noticed a bird landing on the silhouette of an Oak tree next to the roadway.

I had agreed to meet Jasta and Julia for dinner with Alex. The four of us were to begin our ritual racquet ball and Mexican food night. I was tired, but equally eager to share my flying adventures with Jasta. He had earned his wings the prior year and was in the process of building an experimental aircraft. I missed the company of Jasta and Cheryl, but I had promised Alex I would give Jasta's new bride, Julia, a chance.

Those wind chimes continued to sing in my head, so I tuned in the radio to a 1975 hit from Diana Ross, "Do You Know Where You're Going To."

GREATER THAN ONE HUNDRED

*R*acquet ball night moved into the Friday evening position, followed by a trip to our favorite Mexican restaurant. Julia had grown up in Sutter Creek. She was tall with long straight red hair, brown eyes, and she was attractive. She had an athletic physique and was the total opposite of Cheryl. Alex knew everyone, he was the big fish in the little pond. He, Jasta, and Julia were a part of that pond. I was a bit of an outcast, having grown up in the Bay Area. I was the small fish in the large bay. The only saving grace was I had delivered two heirs to Alex's Italian dynasty.

The Mexican restaurant was family owned. We had become acquainted with them over the years, and each week we were warmly greeted by them. The four of us snuggled into a booth. I sat alongside Jasta, and Julia sat opposite me next to Alex. Alex and Jasta would discuss their racquetball game while Julia and I gossiped. The seating seemed cozy, and I tried my hardest to warm up to our new Friday evening cohorts. I sensed being in a cloud around them. Up seemed down. Something wasn't right and the more we hung out, the bigger the cloud grew.

Time drifted by, and our Friday nights turned into every-other-week, then we started meeting once a month, and then we abruptly stopped. I probed Alex regarding our racquetball and Mexican dinner dates. However, Alex continued to make excuses by blaming Jasta. He said Jasta was strange. Jasta was difficult at times. Jasta had quit talking to him, and he had no idea why. When I ran into Jasta at the airport, he would avoid me and look the other way. A very large cumulus cloud engulfed our friendship, and I wasn't instrument rated.

In turn, I rotated 180 degrees and focused on my flying and my children. Bella and Bianca were growing up and my babies had turned into toddlers. With the absence of cohort gatherings, Alex and I continued to grow in opposite directions as well. Our cloud was more like a stratus layer. It was low level, thin and moved in a horizontal direction. I fully submerged myself in my FAA exam. I listened to a private pilot written test syllabus on my audio walk-man. I listened while washing the dishes, vacuuming the carpet, or hanging out with the girls while they watched their favorite cartoons. I had sunk deeper into my world and became less concerned with Alex's.

I was unaware of the true absence of Alex and the true absence of me. I was no longer fumbling through phone bills. I didn't care any longer if Alex had another woman's phone number tucked into his wallet. There were obvious household signs. The curtains would be drawn during the day, or the VHS tracker would read 9999 rather than 0000 after rewinding the tape. When I left in the mornings, I would set it at 0000 by pressing the reset button. When I arrived late in the afternoon, it would read 9999. It was obvious he had been at home watching a movie, alone or otherwise. His late nights became my sanctuary and allowed me study time. When he was home early, he took the girls for bike rides or walks. I remained home while reviewing the principals of flight.

I would get the occasional phone call from our local Blockbuster store that a video was late for return. I would search the house, eventually finding a pornographic movie hidden in the garage cabinet. Alex attempted to hide his sexual syndrome from me. One night I woke late at night to sounds coming from the living room. The oohs-and-the-aahs were too loud, and when I got up to request that he lower the volume, Alex was engaged in his I-can-satisfy-myself-better-than-anyone position. It was awkward, and I backed away. I made my 180-degree turn and buried my head in a pillow. It wasn't the only time. His behavior confused me. When I confronted him, his reply was, "All men do this, Tess. If you ask them, ninety percent will admit to it and ten percent will lie."

We had become two separate people living under the same roof, sleeping in the same bed. My nights would feel lonely had it not been for the streetlight that shone in the sign of a cross. I hung on to that. I pondered more and more about Catholicism. Bella was soon to begin her continued education classes. I would take them to Mass on Sundays; however, Alex refused to go. The three of us would listen, and the girls behaved nicely in church. How could I support this religion and have no knowledge of its teachings?

It wasn't long before I met with the priest and enrolled myself in their adult continued education course. I was willing to be baptized over that same marble font and marry Alex in the church, as promised. It was a challenge, studying flying and Catholicism. But I clung to the diversion of challenges, and I forged on.

One Saturday afternoon, after a class with Father John, I was eagerly excited about our getting married again. Alex's response was deflating. "Why would I marry you in the church, Tess? I already married you once, and I am not going to marry you again!"

Needless to say; the stratus layer grew in intensity, becoming a cumulous-nimbus cloud. My desire to stay with him lessened. I was heartbroken. I knew my place here was not that of a love affair. I filled in the blanks on an application form. I was the good wife, the good mother, the good housekeeper, the good cook, the good laundry service, the good taxi service, the good bookkeeper, and the occasional good lay. Vicki Robust's words lingered in my head, *"He loves you, Tess, but he isn't in love with you."*

Captain Douglass insisted it was time. I was ready to take my FAA private pilot written exam. I decidedly placed the troubled me aside and signed up for a three-day interactive ground school, ending with the written exam. It was conducted at the American Flyers Aviation School on the Hayward Airport grounds, about two hours' drive from Amador

City. The airport's hotel was next to the school, so I reserved a room for two nights. It was showtime, and I had to focus on all the data stored in my head. I was a nervous Nelly, and passing this exam was most important to me. I had failed at a preliminary test months before, and that had forced me into even more intense courses.

I was indeed challenged. The classes commenced early, beginning on a Thursday and concluding on a Sunday. I entered the classroom, taught by John C. Murphy, who was the Assistant Chief Flight Instructor. My eyes scanned the room, which was filled with students. I was the only woman present. It continued to be a man's world, just like my younger days at the night school aviation course and my auto mechanic class. I took a seat in the front row, that way I didn't feel challenged by the male students sitting behind me. I didn't notice them, and it never distracted me from the course. The days were intense and the curriculum extensive.

We covered many categories: Aerodynamics, Aircraft performance, Weather, Navigation, Communications, Airspace requirements, Weight and Balance, and the list goes on and on. Each day we were engulfed in detailed mandatory material, covering eighty-four hours of course data crammed into a thirty-two-hour-crash course. Fortunately, I had covered all this data in a twelve-week course at our local airport. It was a refresher for me, and it fine-tuned my knowledge. At the end of each day, we took a mini test from our instructor. He could then evaluate how each of us was doing and whether we needed one-on-one time with him. Each morning, he returned our tests and mine had a score of one hundred percent. I was pleased, but I was my worst enemy, constantly doubting myself.

At the end of day two, my instructor approached me. He was encouraging me to take the exam on the last day. I agreed, but with great reservation. We broke for lunch, and I contacted Lexie, who was living in nearby Hayward. We had agreed to meet for lunch.

I waited outside the school, along with a handful of male students from my classroom. We discussed the syllabus and the anticipation of our final exam the next day. As we talked, a Harley-Davidson low ride pulled up. The engine wound up, making the silence after it turned off even more still. We watched as the rider removed their helmet.

Her blonde hair fell below her shoulders, and she adorned her face with a big smile. Lexie waved, and I hollered a big hello. I glanced back at the men's jaw-dropping, wide-eyed faces. They looked at me and said, "You are learning to fly airplanes, and your friend rides a Harley?"

"Yes", I answered with a wink. I walked over to Lexie and gave her a big hug. She handed me an extra helmet, and I climbed on back. We rode off for lunch. I took another glance back at the male gallery; they stood frozen like the people in the wax museum at Fisherman's Wharf.

Lexie was my long-lost best friend. Since I was married to Alex, we spent very little time together. I missed her company and her advice. She was an inspiration to me, and she challenged my self-doubt to be strong. "You are smart, Tess, and you can do this!" she would push. We enjoyed our quick lunch, and I agreed to meet with her for dinner after I was done on Sunday. I promised her I would take the test, but again it was with great reservation. I was frightened at the thought of failing.

Sunday arrived, and I was escorted to a testing room for my written exam. Normally, I would have taken the exam on a computer, but on that day the computers were down. I glanced at my instructor and spoke with hesitation, "Maybe I should wait. Perhaps I could study more and come back next week when the computers are up and running?"

Mr. Murphy looked down at me, with a very stern look, "Tess, what do you want? Better than one hundred percent?"

"I guess I am being ridiculous?" I asked.

"Yes, take the test!" he demanded.

I seated myself at a long table. I was given two-and-one-half hours to complete a sixty question, multiple-choice test. The time was ticking by and I continually glanced up at the clock. I was making good time, and with each question I was feeling confident with my answer. I struggled with one. It was a question which I had received different answers for. It involved stalls, and that was not my favorite subject. We had three multiple-choice answers, and two of those could easily be correct. It was a matter of choice, and so I selected one while crossing my fingers.

I finished within the first hour; that could have been a good sign or a bad one. I sweated profusely as I turned in my completed test papers. They would get submitted, and I was told it would be a four hour wait for my results. I left the school and walked around the airport admiring all the airplanes that were tied down. I paused at the empty space that my father's plane once occupied. It took me back to earlier years, when times were much simpler.

~

"DON'T LEAVE ME" I RECALLED POUNDING ON THE CAR WINDOW AS HE taxied away. While sitting on Mother's lap in our station wagon, I had glanced down at my bare feet. My four years had neglected to teach me about losing my shoes.

I took a cross-country trip to Idaho with my father. I was sixteen years old, and my mother hated to fly. We had packed our bags for one week to visit family. My father was loading the plane, and I ran to use the restroom before taking off. As I walked back toward his plane, he had taxied toward me. I walked around the wing and entered behind the propeller's wash. The tower control had radioed to my father, "Watch out for that young girl, walking in your direction!"

My father, with that gleam in his eyes, radioed back, "That girl walking in my direction will be getting into my airplane." He thought that was so funny, allowing the tower controller to think he had picked up a young woman to go flying with him. I remember how ridiculous he was, and I just rolled my eyes at him.

We taxied into position and took off, making our sweeping turn toward the Sierra Nevada Mountains. We had flown directly over Jackson-Westover Field. I remember looking down on it. Little did I know, this would become the base airport I would train at.

~

I STOOD ENTRANCED, AND SUDDENLY I BECAME AWARE OF A MAN'S VOICE hollering at me. I turned to see Mr. Murphy waving me over to the school. I bolted from past to present. Upon entering the school's main doors, I observed my instructor standing aside the front counter. He had a big grin on his face. "You passed, Tess! Would you like to know what your score was?" he quizzed.

I stiffened with my mouth opened. My eyes pivoted back and forth, and my head remotely rocked in the same motion as my uncle's wooden roadrunner. "Ok, no wait. No, I passed, and that's all that matters. No, wait a minute... Yes, I want to know. No, yes, oh okay, what was my score?"

Mr. Murphy, my confident instructor, eyed me up and down. He let out a sigh and responded, "Your score was ninety-eight percent! That means you only missed one question! You topped my class, Tess! You scored higher than anyone else! Can I post your score on my bulletin board? I am so proud of you."

I was stunned and in deep thought. Finally, I responded, "Which question did I miss?"

THE FISH

Southwest Airways was purchased by Howard Hughes in 1970. The Airwest fleet added its newest purchase; a McDonnell Douglas DC-9-30 which Captain Douglass was commissioned to fly, but he would later retire in a Boeing 727. The airline became *Hughes Air West*. Mr. Hughes had made a critical observation; airplanes were much more visible in the air if painted bright yellow. The fleet was repainted, and the company slogan became *Top Banana in the West*.

In time, I made the correlation to the three sections in a banana. Flights would range in destinations to Mexico, Canada, and the western United States. It was during one of his flights from Mexico, with a layover in Los Angeles, that my Captain Angel rescued me from the horrors of custom controls. His four stripes, pencil mustache, and sheepish grin were unmistakably charming. He bared a close resemblance to Howard Hughes. Perhaps Mr. Hughes was influenced by Captain Douglass. After all, they had shared the same hanger at the Oakland Airport hub.

Captain Douglass had chalked up over thirty-one-thousand hours in the air. He was the greatest flying figure I knew. His endless stories captivated me. We would spend hours conversing, and at every flying lesson I ingested a part of his history. He would gaze beyond me, as though looking through a window of time.

He seemed to transform into a young captain, when sharing his struggle to catch *the fish* on the end of his fishing line. It was during a layover in the city by the bay. He stood in the inlet of water, just beyond the runway. Entranced, with his waders on, the big one struggled to get free, and Captain struggled to hang on. Time evaporated, along with the San Francisco mist. Jet airliners screamed above as they made their way over the excited fisherman. And then, as fast as one can sneeze, *the fish* was gone. Captain had lost the battle, and it was at that moment, he had glanced at his watch. He bolted to his car and drove to the airport.

Back then, everyone waited on the captain. He was highly regarded, much like a British nobleman, and his tardiness was nothing new. He rushed to the gate, entered in the aircraft's rear, swiftly walked down the center aisle, and handed his fishing rod to the flight attendant. While still wearing his waders, he disappeared into the cockpit, closing the door. The flight attendant placed the rod in the adjacent cabinet and prepared for take-off. The curious passengers stared at the attendant and finally one spoke up, "Who was that?"

The attendant responded, "That was the captain! Please fasten your seat belts and move your seats into the upright position."

On his last flight into Oakland International Airport, Hughes Airwest planned the customary retirement ceremony on the ground. In anticipation of his late arrival, they had laid out the red carpet, gathered around the tarmac with other captains, first officers, and flight crews. It was the first time, in the history of his career, he was ahead of schedule. He had already landed, had already departed the aircraft, and had already proceeded through the gate. When the airline became aware of the situation, a co-worker hailed him down and demanded that he return to the plane. Everyone quickly gathered to the correct location and lined up outside the aircraft for his retirement ceremony, red carpet and all.

He and his wife Janette had planned on traveling the world upon his retirement. It was the happiness they spoke of whenever they turned in for the night. He, with his endless flying privileges and her with an endless hope in her heart. "She was breathtaking!" he would say. "She could have been a model!" It was shortly afterwards she was diagnosed with breast cancer. He spent all his savings trying to keep her alive. However, just like the battle he had lost with *the fish*, she lost her own battle. Two years later, she passed away. Captain Douglass lived his next twenty years in solitude. When he spoke of her, it was as though it were yesterday. He hung onto her memory; she was *the fish* he would never let go of.

We shared a common interest, my Captain Douglass and me. Although he was forty years my senior, we loved to fly; we loved Karmann Ghias, and we admired Howard Hughes. I shared my life events with him, and at times he shared more than I needed to know. He made me laugh when I was down; he raised me up when I was low. He believed in me and repeatedly said, "You are very intelligent, you can be anything you want."

After passing my written exam, he was the first person I phoned. He commended me and reassured me, "I knew you would pass! I only knew one person who passed with one hundred percent and now you… with a ninety-eight percent! You see? I told you, you are smart. Take a break. Spend time with your family and get back to me in a few days."

I had called Alex next and gave him my good news. He was eager for me to return home. The girls were asking for me, and I missed them terribly. I bailed on dinner with Lexie. I felt guilty for being gone, and so I expediently checked out of my hotel room and made the monumental drive home.

As I entered the freeway, I sank into Captain's stories from 1922. When Jim was a wee lad of four and five, his father would take him to watch brightly colored planes engaging in dogfights and captivating audiences on the ground. The barn-stormer pilots dropped in among the small valley town people of Fresno, California. Jim had drooled for a chance to ride in an airplane. He later worked at local airports, washing and refueling planes. When his family moved to Alhambra, California, he began flying lessons, saving every dollar earned from selling newspapers and pumping gas.

Captain Douglass had a flawless career, except for one incident at the airport by the sea. It was shortly after a landing; he began taxiing to his assigned gate, and the brakes seized. As he and his first officer struggled to regain control of the Boeing 727, Captain Douglass noticed passengers lined up above the gate waving at him through the windows. He was motioning for them to move out of the way, and the more he motioned, the more they waved back. It was the perfect comedy, and it didn't take long for everyone to realize the plane would not stop.

It was like pouring a bubbly glass of champagne, and the fizz rushing over the glass edge with no stopping it. Everyone abruptly made a mad dash away from the windows just as the nose inched its way into the terminal and slowed to a stop. No one was hurt, except the egos of the cockpit crew and the aircraft's nose. Perhaps someone should have rubbed it for good luck. The mishap sounded very familiar. I wouldn't be surprised if Howard Hughes had shared the story with his Hollywood acquaintances.

I made the sweeping turn off Highway 99 and traveled east on Highway 88 toward Amador City. I was one hour from home. I had made it through one-third of my flight training. The next phase would prove to be the most difficult. I reminded myself that I was a mother first and a wife second. Or should I have been a wife first, and a mother second?

I contemplated on what Captain Douglass had reiterated to me; "If you are not flying for a living, Babe, and you absolutely, positively have to be somewhere… drive."

UNEQUIVOCALLY DRIVE

*J*t seemed I was suspended somewhere between heaven and earth. I could only see what appeared to be a window screen; small dots scattered about, shadowing my view of the earth. I could neither see above nor below them. Yet as I fell, the window screen dissipated and my eyes fixed on the celestial lights, twinkling above me, whispering, "I want to go home."

I viewed my daughter Bianca standing beneath me. She was small, and another mirror image of her stood a few feet away, on a cold concrete sidewalk. Her reflection was younger, and yet the two were the same. Both were looking at each other, yet they were not. I continued to fall, and the whispers became louder; "I want to go home." Suddenly, an umbrella opened up, and I grabbed on to the curvature of the handle, and I slowly descended. And then I awoke.

"Wake up, Mommy!" Bella shouted at my bedside. She and Bianca stood alongside me with greeting smiles. I had fallen into a deep sleep and was unaware that Alex had left for work. At times my children were my alarm clock. It was the best, unwritten, unrehearsed and unrecorded wake-up call that one could ever ask for.

~

HOME IS WHERE THE HEART IS, OR SO THEY SAY. WHERE IS THAT HEART and what home does it settle in? I had felt the cold crispness of the sheet beneath me. My body lay facing the bedroom window and just beyond the flowering plum tree, the streetlamp glowed. A full moon rested in the dark sky, creating a Vincent-Van-Gogh-like oil painting. Light showers had dissipated, leaving remnants of gray clouds gently drifting to the east. The nocturnal nightjar birds sang and my heart grieved. I could never let go of the emptiness I felt that night, along with the images of silent children adrift. My mind wandered and Eric Clapton's song lingered. "Tears in Heaven" tore at my heart. I should have embraced that space between the window screen. If I had waited just a bit longer, perhaps it would have opened up. Perhaps I would not have needed that umbrella.

I GATHERED UP MY TWO DAUGHTERS, AND WE SNUGGLED IN BED, BELLA with her Raggie and Bianca with her blue Ellie. "What shall we have for breakfast?" I asked. Bella wanted pancakes, and Bianca wanted paw-cakes. They were precious and deserving.

I rose from bed and put on my robe. Bella ran to the kitchen, taking her usual place at the table with Raggie on her lap. Bianca waited for me to pick her up, and I lovingly carried her to the kitchen. It was the beginning of a new day, and my dream made me wonder. I had a tendency to second guess myself. I questioned whether I was ready for my private pilot check-ride.

The drive to Sutter Creek that morning was still. The trees lightly brushed against each other and the coolness of November shed its morning dew. Fall was abundant while leaves radiated in brilliant yellows and orange. I arrived at my in-law's home and escorted Bella and Bianca into the Italian mansion. Their grandparents' welcoming demeanor was well received. I was happy the girls loved visiting them. I had given my daughters a long hug, followed with a kiss, and upon leaving I noticed the disapproving eye of Angelo.

He walked me to my car and leaned in, just as I was about to start the car. "Why are you doing this, Tess? Why are you spending all of Alex's hard-earned money for a pilot's license you will never use? You cannot make a living of it, and I think it is unwarranted and selfish."

His words were hurtful, and I tried my best to shake them off. "I too work hard, Angelo. In case you hadn't noticed, I earned this equally, and I have spent countless hours preparing for this day. It will be the greatest accomplishment of my life. I am thankful for the family's support, and I am disappointed that I do not have yours. Thank you for watching over the girls while I take my check-ride today. I sincerely appreciate that." I waved him off and pulled out of their driveway.

I hadn't noticed the winds picking up. My eyes only caught glimpses of the pine trees bending and swaying, while the Douglas's squirrels clung to their massive trunks; their tails twitching from left to right. I tried to focus on the flight, and not on my father-in-law.

Alex was more like his mother, but in time I would grow to appreciate and understand Angelo. After all, he was the aviator-navigator who jumped from a bomber airplane over Yugoslavia. He knew the dangers of flying.

I was merely his daughter-in-law, who bore two children and managed the books for their company. He regarded me in the same way as Alex did, a good fit. On their application form, I had neglected to fill out the line for miscellaneous remarks. I had forgotten to reveal my future goal is to become a pilot. Perhaps they would not have accepted me, and perhaps Angelo was correct. Maybe I would not amount to much, but maybe… just maybe… I would.

I arrived at Westover Field and parked next to my hangar. I prepared my airplane for the flight to Calaveras County Airport, or better known as Maury Rasmussen Field. I had an appointment with a flight examiner for my knowledge test and check-ride. I attached the toe-bar to the nose wheel and pulled my plane out. I closed up the hangar, jumped into the cockpit, and ran through my checklist. I noticed the windsock pivoting back and forth. The American flag was rippling in the wind. What began as a calm day was changing into a blustery day.

I taxied into position, made my announcement on the open frequency, and checked for air traffic. It was silent. I pulled onto runway 19 and departed straight out. As I gradually lifted off the asphalt, the winds aloft became stronger. I contemplated the weather and began my self-doubt syndrome. I recalled Captain Douglass's words, "You are the pilot in command. Listen to your gut, and if it doesn't feel right, it probably isn't. But most important, Babe... when you find yourself in any given situation, always remember your first and foremost job is to *fly the airplane*. Never, ever, forget that."

I continued flying south to Rasmussen Field. It was a short flight—about twenty minutes. The airport had an elevation of 1,325 feet and was surrounded by mountains. It sat on a plateau with three sides dropping two hundred feet. The runway length of 3,603 feet by 60 feet was a welcoming level asphalt. The air typically ran straight down the runway, with a preferred right-hand pattern for runway 31. As I approached the airport, I glanced down at the wind direction indicator, favoring the preferred runway. The windsock, sitting mid-way of the runway, was straight out, indicating a strong head wind.

I began my G.U.M.P.S. landing procedures, before entering a right-hand, down-wind approach. I announced my position and listened to the captain's whisper in my ear. I lowered my wing flaps ten degrees, then twenty, and made my right base turn lowering to thirty degrees. I made my final turn and lined up with the runway, focusing on the third line. I usually came in high, and a slip maneuver was comfortable for me. It was different this time.

I had been warned about the *sinker* at the end of this runway. Due to the terrain drop, the wind would carry down, just as water would and spill over the edge. "Don't get in the sinker, Babe. Come in high at this airport, stay above it. Many planes have sunk into the ravine and crashed. You never want to miss a perfectly good runway." Captain reiterated.

I was alone, and the comfort of my missing co-pilot was itching at me. I watched as the runway rose very fast in my windshield. I increased power, and the runway continued its rise. I pushed the throttle in, and before I knew it, the throttle was buried at its maximum input; I had no more power. The third line was impossible to land on. I had focused on the runway's edge and looked beyond it, watching the far end of the runway. I touched down just before the numbers, and reduced power to idle, braking heavily. It was too close for comfort. I had barely made the asphalt. The stall horn did not sound, and my speed was faster than usual. I taxied to the far end and made my way over to the tie-down area for transients. I shut down my airplane when I noticed the examiner standing outside his office watching me. I shuddered to think he was watching the entire time. It was not my finest hour.

The ground winds were howling, and my airplane was rocking back and forth as I struggled to tie down the wings and tail. Tumble weeds rolled across the tarmac, and my hat blew off as I walked toward the office. The examiner caught it and waved me over. He had a big grin on his face as he opened the office door, allowing me to enter first. I glanced up at him and then quickly back at the ground, wondering what his thoughts may have been.

"Well, you made it. You must be, Tess?" he asked.

"Yes, I am. I am so nervous! That was a bit scary out there. I was about to make a go-around, and abort my landing, but I hung on and here I am!" I managed to say with a half-smile.

"Yes, you are. I would suggest, with a strong wind such as that, thirty degrees of flaps is unnecessary. It creates more drag, and drag is not what you needed. You did a great job, though. I watched the entire approach and other than that… it was flawless."

I had made my way over to his student desk and took a seat. He gave me numerous scenarios for take-off and landings. I was quizzed on weight and balance, along with fuel calculations. He had given me a weather briefing for today, with gusts ranging from twenty-five to fifty-knots. My eyebrows unexpectedly rose, and I pondered the consequences of those gusts. I seemed to pass the knowledge exam with flying colors, and I reminisced about my auto mechanics teacher. He had taught me the principals of the automobile engine, which came in handy when I was quizzed about the aircraft engine. He had encouraged me, as did my Captain.

We walked out to the airplane, and he observed my walk-around inspection. He asked that I leave the plane tied down, and we entered the cockpit to discuss more about the aircraft engine. As he questioned me, I interrupted him. "So, I want to understand this process today. I am the pilot in command, and if at any time you take over on the controls, I fail the test. Is that correct?"

He responded, "Yes, that is correct. The only time I will take over, is when we perform unusual attitudes, which you will have to take over and recover the plane. That will be the only time I touch the controls."

I questioned again, "Ok, so the winds are pretty strong. I have final say about the flight?"

"Yes, I know it seems to be a very strong wind, but let's take off and fly around a bit. If you think it's too difficult, we can come back and land. We can always fly another day. What do you say, Tess? Shall we give it a go?" he asked as another tumble weed rolled by.

I had the feeling of uneasiness. My eyes scanned the wings rocking up and down, tugging on the tie-down chains. I glanced at the airport windsock. It was inflated to its capacity. I tapped my fingers on the control wheel and let out a deep breath. I heard the words silently passing through my brain, "If you absolutely, positively, unequivocally have to be somewhere, drive."

"We are not flying today. The winds are too strong," I commanded.

"Are you sure, Tess? We could just give it a go and see what happens? I watched you land, and I am sure you can handle it?" He persisted.

"No, we are not going," I decided–without a doubt.

"Ok, are you sure?" he asked again.

Agitation crept into my cool attitude, "Yes, I am sure. I am pilot in command and we are grounded."

He smiled. He reached over to shake my hand. I hesitated. "Good job, Captain! If we had attempted to fly, in these conditions, I would have failed you. The current winds exceed the limitations of this aircraft. I wanted to test you on how well you might handle pressure. Passengers may pressure you into going and intimidate you into thinking you are afraid or unable to handle it. But you must always set their words aside. Safety is number one, and you are the one to ensure it. I am very proud of you. Tell me something, Tess. How will you get home today?"

I had thought to give Alex a ring, but he was working. I telephoned Captain Douglass. I grinned as he answered the phone. "Guess what, Captain? I am going to need a ride. Can you drive over to Rasmussen Field and get me?"

I realized when I hung up the phone that I absolutely, positively, unequivocally had to be somewhere, and we were going to drive.

THE TRUTH

$\mathcal{T}$he truth. What is the actual truth and when can one, without a doubt, actually see and hear it? I have always sought out the truth, but not without remorse. I continued to have misgivings about Alex and his ability, or lack thereof, to be a faithful husband. Too many truths had been revealed in one form or the other.

I drove down Main Street in Amador City and glimpsed Alex alongside a building, holding hands with a woman. They had jumped back behind the brick wall, as though I would not have noticed. But I did. I always noticed and that would be my curse in life. It was the minor details. Alex's company vehicle was parked just down the street from the old brick building. The analysis of a given situation and my ability to dissect its meaning gave way to the shadows of my past. They would slip in with absolute darkness, and I was reminded of my constant mistakes.

～

JANUARY 28TH, 1986. I WAS IN MY FIRST TRIMESTER WITH BELLA. I remember sitting in the kitchen while eating breakfast. I was alone, and we had a small television sitting on an antique wooden step stool. I watched the black and white images of the Space Shuttle Challenger navigating its way to the crest of our everyday horizon. I watched as the shuttle split into three sections, just like a banana, only it divided into white trails against the blue sky. My eyes teared up, and I sat trying to decipher what was happening. The CNN commentator, Tom Miniter, was silent. Sounds from a panicked audience became the backdrop to a catastrophic failure. It was soon revealed that all seven astronauts lost their lives in the explosion. I watched as the information unfolded, and the truth eventually surfaced.

That evening, President Ronald Reagan spoke to our nation. He was candid, yet compassionate with his words. He addressed the children who had been watching the launch in their classrooms. He consoled the families and the American citizens who had worked so hard to make this happen. He reminded us about the explorers of our past, and that without exploration we would not grow. Our expeditions can lead us to great successes and great sorrows.

My heart was on that day in January. My own explorations had led me down many avenues. My desire to fly high above the horizons, and revel in its glory, was not without heavy consequences. Bella was growing in my belly, and I was about to become a mother. I stood looking out the kitchen window. The shallow sounds of news broadcasters channeled against heavy currents of the heart.

I wondered about the Elderberry hedge and its legendary scent. The evils had yet to be warded off, but I remained hopeful. I caught sight of the blue sky, and I sensed a calmness in its depths. Seven souls dissipated, fusing into the universe of space and time. For their loved ones left behind, they became their own voids–a reminder of our fourth dimension of consciousness or spirit.

THE WOMAN AGAINST THE BRICK WALL WAS LATER REVEALED. HER NAME was Mary, and we had met when I dated William. William and James had shared a condo with Mary. She had long dark brown hair and was very attractive. Rumor had it she and Alex were carrying on at her apartment, which was on the old road heading out of Jackson. I drove by there once and noticed Alex's pickup truck parked outside. I didn't have the nerve to stop. I looked the other way.

Then there was the woman who lived along the creek who lived in an older home painted a barn red. She drove an old 1950-something pickup. It was similar to the one my father had when I was living in San Leandro. She was the local bootie call. I had received a phone call from a family friend shortly after we were married. He asked if Alex and I were separated? I was curious where this was going. He told me about his late-night bootie call drive over to her house. When he arrived, Alex's truck was parked outside.

Then there was the time when Angelo and Alma had traveled to San Diego. Alex and I were keeping an eye on their house, and Francesca stayed the night when she was available. I had purchased some new clothes from a small boutique in Jackson. Alex and I were to fly out the next morning and join Angelo and Alma in San Diego for a small business owners' convention. I decided to use Alma's ironing board and touch up the blouses I had purchased. She kept a sewing room upstairs, and her ironing table was much more accessible than mine.

The mansion had two staircases. One was near the kitchen, and the other by the entrance. I recall climbing the stairs near the entrance, which led to a sitting room lined with books. There were three bedrooms, one bath, a sewing room, and a pool table centered in the game room. Each room faced the sitting area and a tapestry rug rested upon the wooden floor.

The rooms showcased the same furniture as when the children were small. Alex and his brother Salvatore's room had two twin beds made of cherry wood headboards, footboards, and matching nightstands. The eldest, Amalia, had a room with a brass queen-size bed. Francesca had a smaller room with an oak four-post full-size bed. All the rooms were decorated in antique furnishings. The paintings that hung on the walls were from the early 1900s, along with black and white images from World War II.

As my hand slid along the decorative wooden handrail, I could hear an electric heater running. I was puzzled, and upon reaching the top of the staircase; I followed it into Amalia's room. It was on the floor, radiating near the bed, removing the chill and awaiting someone to occupy the room. The central heat had been set on low, and I was concerned to see an electric heater running by itself. I unplugged it and stood scanning the room, taking in the details of the stage in my mind. Alex had announced that morning he would be at an Italian Society meeting in the evening and would get home late. My analytical mind put two and two together, and I sensed what he was up to.

The phone rang at the small writing desk next to the bookcases. Coincidently, it was Alex. He wanted to know when I would go home, and he reminded me about his upcoming meeting.

"You are not going!" I shouted. "I just unplugged the electric heater in the upstairs bedroom. Your rendezvous is not happening, Alex. I have had enough."

There was that momentary silence on the other end of the phone line. "I have no idea what you are talking about? Francesca is staying there, perhaps she plugged in the heater for herself!" he insisted.

"Really? You are going to blame this on your sister? You are staying home tonight. I don't care if you have a meeting. I am putting my foot down. Not tonight, Alex. Do you understand?" I demanded.

I hung up the phone and ironed my blouses. It was all I could do to remain calm. My mind tumbled and my heart ached. I was a good wife, and I was unwilling to remain the *look-the-other* way wife. I heard the door close downstairs, and Francesca hollered as she entered the dining room. "I'm upstairs!" I responded. Francesca joined me in the sewing room, and I inquired about the heater. "Did you plug in the wall heater in Amalia's room?" I asked.

"Hell no," she answered. "Why would I do that? I'm sleeping downstairs in Mom and Dad's room. I hardly ever come up here, Tess." Her eyes meeting mine.

I knew he was full of shit. I didn't need to ask her, but I wanted to be sure and now I knew. "Alex is up to his old tricks. He was planning on meeting someone here tonight. I suppose I could have waited to catch him, but then again you would have caught him. Would you have told me?" I questioned.

"Well," she hesitated. "I heard from somewhere, that he had been fooling around with someone. I would have told you if you asked me, but it was a rumor, Tess. What can I say? He isn't capable of being faithful. What are you going to do?" she asked.

"I am going home, Francesca. I will see you later." I descended the stairs and walked out of the Italian mansion.

I thought about that movie as I drove home. The one that hit the box office in 1972. It was nominated for an academy award. At the end of the movie, a hand surfaced in the chilling deep blue lake as Jon Voight awakened from his nightmare. My mind shifted to that clear blue sky above, and then I imagined Alex in that queen-size brass bed sinking that low. And then it came to me, *Deliverance*. It was about the truth, and just like the electric heater glowing in the empty room waiting for occupancy; the truth will always surface.

BUMP CITY

*L*ake Tahoe was only a few hours' drive from Amador City. Numerous mud slides had closed Interstate 80, preventing traffic from traveling to the lake. The lesser traveled Highway 88 was open, and Alex wanted to take advantage of the low attendance at the casinos. It was a clear, crisp day in February 1986. We had made our reservations at Harrah's Casino and Hotel for a two-night stay. Alex enjoyed playing black-jack, and I preferred the shows.

The six-foot walls of snow lined the highway. It was one of the highest recorded snow falls in years, and the view of the Sierra Nevada Mountains was spectacular. We traveled in Alex's four-wheel-drive truck, and I admired Silver Lake as we passed it. The lake was frozen over and memories of my Brazilian friends, Sofia and Luiza, came to mind.

~

WE SAILED ON THE LAKE. THE THREE OF US ZOOMED ACROSS THE DEEP blue water. When the wind had ceased, I admired Thunder Mountain's statuesque presence. Luiza spoke up, "This is what I imagined California would look like!" We absorbed our moment of silence, and I waited for a wind to catch our sail.

Luiza brought out her camera from her nap-sack. She snapped photos of the mountain. With hesitation, and a frown on her face, she looked up at me and said, "My camera stop-pi-did."

Her Brazilian accent was pally, and I remember responding "No, Luiza your camera stopped."

She smiled back at me and said, "Yes, it stop-pi-did!" and we all laughed.

AS WE ROUNDED THE HIGHWAY'S CURVE, WE APPROACHED KIRKWOOD Meadows Ski Resort. I admired the skiers making their way down the black diamond face. My skiing days had taken a back seat in life, just as so many things do. The rustic Kirkwood Bar and Lounge was a good stop for breakfast. It was a popular favorite for those traveling on the highway.

When we entered the lounge–it was a bit like going back in time. The old wood plank floor creaked as we made our way over to an eating area. Patrons sat at the bar and turned their heads to check out who entered their domain. The walls were lined with old vintage metal signs, taking me back to a much simpler time–a time when getting your first kiss seemed like a milestone. And yet knowing what I had learned since then, if anything, was how unimportant it really was. Alex made my life complicated, as did most men. Except for Elio; he never made a commitment, and so he never broke his promises. He was there when I returned from Brazil, just as he said he would be. But not in the way I was hoping. Those were my expectations, not his.

As Alex ordered our breakfast. He ordered a Bloody-Mary. I had quit drinking and since this would be my firstborn child; I was careful not to jeopardize it. Alex was a terrible drunk. He was the guy who hadn't learned his limitations. Once he started, he would continue until he was falling down. It was another characteristic I had come to detest. In my mind, I had to stop comparing him to Elio. I mentioned nothing about him to Alex. Alex had no idea he even existed. It was better that way. It was a way to forget him, although I never did. He would linger there in my fourth dimension, floating in and out.

Highway 88 followed through Hope Valley, and in the fall, brilliant yellow and orange leaves showered the branches of willow and aspen trees as far as one can see. The trees were barren now, and the memory of its beauty hovered in my mind. Lake Tahoe was breathtaking as you dropped down in elevation into its surroundings. The chilling blue lake with its depth of 1,644 feet edged against the pine trees that resembled flocked Christmas trees. I shook the vision of a hand rising from its waters.

Cabins lined Pioneer Trail as we maneuvered through town. I noticed numerous snow men in the yards along with cords of firewood near their doorsteps. Smoke circled up from their A-framed cabin chimneys. Heavenly Ski Resort's renowned terrain was the perfect backdrop. The trail ended at Harrah's Casino and we pulled into the valet-parking area. Alex tossed the keys to a parking attendant as we made our way in.

The lobby had changed little since our honeymoon at Harrah's. It was a blow to my expectation, and I wanted to forget it happened. As Alex and I entered the elevator, he selected the fourth floor. I stared at the illuminated sixteenth floor button.

WE HAD RESERVED LUCILLE BALL'S PENTHOUSE SUITE FOR OUR honeymoon night. It was a corner room with panoramic windows. There were three bedrooms, three bathrooms, a full bar, and a kitchen. There was a dining room and a large sectional couch in a sunken living room; we even had a butler at our disposal. I had invited a small group of friends to join us for dinner and celebrate our union in the suite.

Lexie and her date joined us, along with many friends from Jackson. We spent many hours in the casino, ending at Harveys Seafood Buffet. Alex was drinking his usual non-stop alcohol, and I became tired and bored. Lexie, her date, and I made our way back up to the suite. They kept me company while I waited for Alex to return. Looking back, it perplexes me why Alex insisted on a penthouse suite. We spent very little time in it. Lexie had become very perturbed. They eventually left, and I retired for the night.

Alex and his best friend Nick arrived in our room very late, and they were equally drunk. I was trying to sleep during those wee hours. Their conversation and laughter had awoken me. I tip-toed from the bedroom and peered into the living room. Alex hung on the interior window ledge, peering down at the lake, looking a lot like Spiderman. Nick laughed. The phone rang next to my bed, and I scurried to answer it. Nick's wife was calling and asking for him. It seemed I wasn't the only one upset over the situation. I hollered out to Nick, but he ignored her call. I couldn't imagine anyone spending their wedding night in the company of a couple of drunk men. Alex was oblivious.

THE ELEVATOR DOOR OPENED TO THE FOURTH FLOOR. I FOLLOWED AS Alex led us to our room. I paused and lightly brushed my belly. Times had changed and so had my body. I was in too deep now. I had made a commitment, and I would try my best to honor it.

"Hey, Tess. I noticed Tower of Power is playing downstairs tonight. You said you knew the trumpet player in the band, maybe you could introduce me?" he said with a laugh. Alex didn't believe the story. He was sure I didn't know him, and he was toying with me. "You knew him in band camp, right?" Alex continued with his mocking laugh.

I raised one eyebrow and gave him the Katie look. "I would love to go. I will call and reserve us a ticket!" I responded.

We dined at Harrah's Friday's Station for steak and seafood before the show. Tower of Power was playing in the Cabaret room downstairs near the casino bar. The view at night from the restaurant was mystifying. I was mystified. I seemed to live in a constant state of bamboozlement. I had wanted to hang on to every wonderful memory (not a picture window) and in doing so, I missed the moments. I can't even remember what I ate for dinner or if it was romantic.

The Cabaret room had patrons lining up for the show. A row of people formed alongside the bar, and we took our places with all the others. As we stood waiting, I noticed a familiar face sitting at the bar. I wasn't sure, but it looked like Fred Abrams, the trumpet player. I smiled at Alex and excused myself, "I'll be right back!"

I approached Fred with hesitancy and tapped him on the shoulder. He looked up at me from beneath his large eyeglasses and bushy mustache. It had been a long time, and I wasn't sure if he would remember me. "Hi Fred, it's Tess Hamilton! Remember me from band camp?"

Fred studied me for a moment, and then he stood. "Oh my gosh, Tess. It has been a long time. How are you? You look great. Are you alone? Where are you living now?" he asked.

I had glanced over at Alex, and I couldn't help but notice the scowl on his face.

"I am with my husband. Let me wave him over and I will introduce you. We are staying here at Harrah's. It's so good to see you, Fred. You look the same! I can't wait to hear you play tonight." I gushed. I motioned for Alex to come over.

He seemed irritated. "Tess, we are losing our place in line!" Alex stepped out of line.

I introduced Alex to Fred Abrams. Fred was kind enough to shake hands with Alex, and Alex seemed to be embarrassed. They exchanged light conversation with some awkwardness. I think the good Lord was paying attention that evening. I was being vindicated, and it felt good.

Fred excused himself and we were escorted into the Cabaret lounge for the show. Alex and I were seated at a small table near the front, thanks to Fred. The curtains opened, and the band began playing their hit song "Down to the Nightclub." I glanced over at Alex and smiled.

He winked and raised his glass, "Cheers, Tess!"

I returned the smile and rested my hands on my belly. I thought I had felt a flutter that night. Perhaps my Bella was dancing along with the music. "Cheers," I whispered to our baby.

I looked up and noticed Fred smiling. His familiar face transported me back to band camp. My immaturity and insecurities had clouded my ambitions during my youthful years. We were safely tucked away in the Santa Cruz Mountains of Northern California, without a care in the world. I had watched Fred from afar in admiration of his musical skills as they resonated in the Chapel at Camp Redwood Glen.

My eyes regained focus on the Tower of Power Band. Fred had become a well-known Grammy and Emmy nominated arranger and trumpeter. He dipped his trumpet with a wink as they played the next song, "So Very Hard to Go."

WINGS

*I*t was November 13, 1993, when I pulled out of my garage. The familiar streetlamp was still glowing in the early morning hours. The slight waxing of the crescent moon shined from beyond the rolling hills. It was still just as the children were when I left them sleeping in their beds. Alley had waved me off, and I recall the nervousness that rolled into my head. Today I would attempt, one more time, my check-ride at Rasmussen Airport.

"It is time!" Captain announced. We had spent countless hours practicing for this day. I drove to Westover Field with such enthusiasm, mixed with an element of self-doubt. It was another big day, and one I had only dreamed about in my life.

I pulled alongside my hanger and parked. The American flag had stalled, and that was a good sign. I pulled out my airplane and did the usual walk-around inspection. I jumped into the plane and hollered out the window, "Clear!" before starting my engine. The engine hummed as I ran through my checklist. I glanced around the cockpit and confirmed everything I needed was there. I taxied to the preferred runway 19. The sky was clear, and it appeared I was the only person at the airport. The radio was silent.

I taxied to the run-up area, ran through my take-off checklist, and cleared the sky for any air traffic. It was a go, and the exhilaration crept its way from my toes to my fingertips. I announced my departure and taxied into position. I released the brakes and gently pushed the throttle in. The air was heavily oxygenated, and the engine performed soundly. My airplane lifted off the asphalt as though it wanted to fly all by itself. I was committed. My straight-out departure, heading south, was flawless.

The surrounding terrain, along with the small shops lining Main Street in Jackson, slept. The wisps of smoke filtered out of the residential chimneys. I flew by Butte Mountain and over the cool rapids of Mokelumne River, checking my instruments with quick glances. The view of Lake Camanche faded as I flew further south. Within minutes, I could see Rasmussen's runway, which was undeniably recognizable.

I reported my approach over the radio and entered the right-hand landing pattern, which favored runway 31. I tucked into my right base position and assessed the altitude with the third line of the runway. I moved the flaps from 20 to 30 degrees. I made my turn from base to final and focused on the third line. There wasn't a sinker that day. If I had been sailing in my sailboat, I would have been dead in the water. What would have been a bad situation for a sailboat was a perfect situation for flying.

I heard the whisper of Captain Douglass, "Now, Tess! Look at the end of the runway and let it gradually come up in your windshield." My eyes followed the far runway's edge, and slowly it moved up in my view. I gradually pulled back on the throttle and brought the nose up, ever so slightly. The soft hum of the stall horn quivered, and I touched down smoothly, the nose wheel gently landing last. I slowed to the taxi-way entrance and stopped. "Bring those flaps up before proceeding!" his whisper reminded.

My flight examiner, Rob Davidson, stood watching, and that time I felt more confident about my landing. He waved me over to the transient area, and I parked my ship. I locked my control wheel, chocked the wheels, and walked over to his office. "Today's the day," I told myself. Weather would not be a defining factor.

We spent little time reviewing the verbal knowledge portion. We had covered that at my last appointment. Rob focused on the weather, winds aloft, and our flight plan. It was time to go, and my stomach was queasy. I remember feeling the doubt syndrome closing in. "Fear is what keeps you alive, Tess! Don't ever forget that," Captain Jim would say. He was ingrained in me. His teachings were locked within my subconscious.

I was observed as I executed my walk-around inspection. I was asked numerous questions along the way. We seated ourselves in the cockpit, again Rob quizzed me about the instruments and reviewed my flight plan. I ran through my usual checklists and hollered, "Clear," before starting the engine.

"Let's go flying!" he said.

We taxied to the run-up area, and I prepared for take-off. I announced our departure and taxied into position and held. As instructed, I executed a full-power take-off, inching my throttle forward to full power, releasing my brakes, and powering down the runway. The plane lifted off with ease, and we headed into the sky toward the San Joaquin Valley.

Rob was a calm examiner. He seemed to direct with ease and confidence. He displayed a pleasing demeanor while we flew. I executed and recovered from numerous maneuvers along the way. We flew to Stockton Metropolitan Airport. It was a controlled airport, which means it has a tower. Unlike my base airport, you needed permission to enter their airspace, and contact the control tower operators. Rob observed my communication skills upon entry. I had been cleared for runway 11R, a much shorter runway. Rob had instructed me to make a short-field landing and then execute a go-around (which means I do not exit the runway).

I had announced my straight-in approach and instructed the tower I would be practicing a *touch-and-go*. After getting my clearance, I executed both without any hiccups. Rob then instructed me to proceed straight out and cancel my go-around with the tower. It was approved, and we flew straight out and back toward the Valley.

It was stall time, and a feeling of uneasiness crept in. "Ok, Tess, put this plane in a full stall!" Rob requested.

I cleared the area above and below us, making sure there weren't any planes near us. I eased the control wheel back, reducing power, and continued nose up until the plane shuddered. The stall horn whistled, and I could feel the control wheel turn to mush. The plane broke its ability to sustain lift, and the nose dropped. I immediately recovered. I looked over at Rob and he had one eyebrow raised. "Ok, Tess. Now let's get this plane in a full stall. You recovered too quickly. One more time, let's go!" he requested.

I reluctantly set up for another stall demonstration. I cleared the area, again. I pulled back on my control wheel, again. I reduced power to idle, again. I waited for the quiver and the mush feeling in my hands. The stall horn blew, and the nose dropped. I recovered with a gentle recovery and power. I looked over at him again, and he was smiling. "Great job! Let's go home," he motioned.

During our return flight, I realized we did not execute any ground reference maneuvers. I was okay with that, and later I found out it was because my pattern work at Stockton Metropolitan Airport reflected those. Emergency landings and procedures were discussed, but the inevitable execution was remaining.

We flew over the mountain range just west of Rasmussen Airport, when Rob announced, "Ok, Tess. You just lost your engine and all your electronics have ceased working. You have no power, no flaps and no radio. Land this airplane, without the use of these, and head to the nearest airport. You only have one shot at the given runway, and you have a full plane of passengers." He pulled back my throttle to engine idle, and I immediately knew, under no circumstances was I allowed to touch it.

I immediately dipped my right-wing tip and turned toward Rasmussen Airport. I was very high, and I knew I had plenty of altitude. It was glider mode time, and this was the most difficult emergency landing one could have, especially during a check-ride. I could not radio my approach, so I scanned the sky for air traffic and prayed no one was nearby. I executed a left base approach and realized I needed my flaps to help control my speed. Since I wasn't allowed to use them, I entered a long final approach and use my slip technique. I began to slip the airplane, but the runway was still coming up fast, and I was still very high.

"Use that slip, Babe, to quickly get rid of altitude without gaining airspeed!" I heard the whisper of Captain Douglass. I had decisions to make, and I assessed my difficulty to touch down. I relaxed a bit on the slip (thinking I would not be able to land) and that's when Rob spoke up, "You have one shot at this runway. It would be a pity to miss it with a plane full of passengers!"

I threw my plane into an aggressive slip maneuver, and I forced that plane onto the runway. I landed almost mid-way, but I landed. It was fast and hard. I heavily applied the brakes and slowed to the runway's end. My knees shook and my palms were sweating. I remember how relieved I was to be on the ground. I glanced at Rob and he announced, "Congratulations, Tess Hamilton, you are officially a pilot! Let's taxi over to the transient area. I will need to complete your paperwork."

I glanced over to the transient parking area, and I saw Captain Jim Douglass and his cohort, Captain Wes Ament. They stood outside the office waving at me. I realized there was a good chance they had been watching me as I came into land. Both had big smiles on their faces. That was when I lost it. Tears began to flow, and the realization hit me. I had received my wings. I had accomplished the second hardest task ever given to me.

After parking, locking and securing my ship, Captain Douglass approached me. He shook my hand and gave me a big hug. "You did it, Babe. I told you, if you put your mind to it, you can do anything. You just have to work hard for it. Congratulations! Now, let's go have some lunch. You must be starving!" he announced.

We drove into Angels Camp for lunch. Jim, Wes, and I were seated in a small window booth near the entrance of their favorite diner. As we looked over the menu, an elderly couple entered. They made a beeline toward us. The husband spoke first, "Hi Jim and Wes! This is my wife, Alice. Alice, these are the two pilots I talk about all the time."

Alice responded, "It is so nice to meet you. I hear so much about you both, almost every day. Now I can finally put a face to the stories!"

Jim and Wes smiled, and after exchanging some small talk, the couple walked away and were seated at another table. Jim then looked at

Wes and asked, "Who the hell was that?" Wes responded, "I don't know, but I can tell you his wife's name!" They both laughed.

There were those two Muppets again, Statler and Waldorf. I could picture Statler as Jim and Waldorf as Wes, each wearing a captain hat and four stripes on their shoulders. It was an end to a perfect day.

PRINCIPALS OF FLIGHT

I had received my wings twelve years before getting the call. Life passes before our windshields and time changes everything. Choices had to be made, and as with most decisions in life, remorse or consequences inevitably set in.

Bella was attending her first year at Chico State University. Bianca was a sophomore in high school. I purchased a two-story home in Jackson and I had left Alex years prior. I will avoid divulging the drama of our nasty divorce. I won't go into detail about how he attempted to make me look like a gold-digger in court.

When Alex and I had separated, I received numerous phone calls from family members asking me what had happened? My response was, and continued to be, "One day I will share my journey with you. It is all written in a book, and right now is not the time to share it."

I wondered when that would actually happen. When would I find the strength and courage to share my journey? When would I be able to open up and reveal the darkest secrets of my life? Would I be able to? Who would care, and why would they read it?

The thoughts ran through my head as I sat in a chair, in a room, at our local hospital. Captain Douglass had suffered a massive stroke. I had received the phone call that he was in the ICU. He was unable to eat or breathe on his own. He couldn't speak, and he had lost the ability to move his entire left side. I watched him as he struggled to make sense of it all; his eyes moved about the room, and then his search ceased when his eyes settled on me.

I spoke to him as though he could hear me, but I wasn't certain he could. I spent hours reading to him and filling him in about current events. The World Series was airing on the television in his room. I would glance up as the Chicago White Sox's battled it out with the Houston Astros. Chicago swept Houston in the first four games. It was a shut out for the 101st edition.

He had grown close to my children and me over the past thirteen years. He knew everything about my life, and he knew why Alex and I divorced. He was the grandfather I never had, and although he did not like hearing that, it was true. He completed me in a way no one else had. He believed in me and never once did he judge me negatively. Jim had shifted from being my flight instructor to becoming my best pal.

I watched as Jim struggled for months, deteriorating week by week. His family had to make the difficult decision to remove the feeding tube and oxygen supply. The doctor said he would never improve, and his quality of life would never be better than what it was. He would forever be in bed and never speak another word. He would be attached to machines as long as his body held out. They painfully decided to remove all life supporting devices. They were told he may last ten days at most.

I visited his bedside every evening after work. There were moments when I couldn't read anymore. I became lost at the idea of losing him. He was forty years older than me, and if I was lucky enough to live as long as he did, that would mean I had forty more years to live.

I hovered over him, looked into his eyes and said, "I hate my job. Life sucks. I can't imagine living without you, Jim." I sobbed. I couldn't hold it back any longer, so I buried my head in my hands. Then, I recall feeling something. I raised my head and Jim had lifted his right hand and patted me on the cheek. His eyes spoke to me, "It's okay, Babe." I cupped his hand in mine and I knew. I knew he could hear me.

Bianca and her best friend, Katie, wanted to have dinner out that Sunday evening in November 2005. We drove to Sacramento to their favorite restaurant, TGIF. The girls were not old enough to drive yet, but both were eager to learn. Getting into harmless mischief became a routine for us. They were inseparable. It seemed Katie was continually sleeping over at our house, or Bianca slept at hers. That evening was no different. Katie was bunking down with us. It was raining as we drove home and dark by the time we arrived at our house. It was also a school night, so I instructed the girls to get showered and ready for bed. Jim weighed heavily on my mind, so I decided to make a trip to the hospital. "I will be gone an hour or so, call if you have an emergency!" I instructed Bianca.

It was a short three-minute drive to the local hospital. The clouds had moved to the east and the light showers had left their footprint along the roads. Saturated fallen leaves were scattered over the hoods of parked vehicles as I entered the parking area. The dampness sent a chill through me. The moon above served as a spotlight as I locked my car door.

I entered the sliding door entry and took the elevator to Jim's floor. When I walked into his room, I sensed something was very wrong. Jim was gasping for air, and he was alone. I hailed a nurse who was walking by, and she said he was close to the end. Evidently his breathing was part of starving to death. I noticed his eyes were caked shut from dehydration. I grabbed a washcloth and rinsed it in warm water. I applied it gently over his eyes and cleaned his eyelids. He opened his eyes and fixed them on mine. I spoke to him as calmly as I could and guided him through his breathing. He slowed his breath, and before long he was breathing normally. I lowered the arm rail and sat next to him on the bed.

"It's okay to let go, Jim. I am here with you and you are not alone. I will stay as long as you need. Your wife Janette is waiting for you, along with your mother and father. I will be okay. You don't need to worry. I love you, Jim." I whispered.

I lifted his head and slid my arm underneath. I embraced him as long as he needed. I continued to assure him, but I knew. I knew I was right where I was supposed to be, except this time he was listening to me explain the principals of a different flight.

I looked out the window and noticed the Gibbous Moon shining over the silhouette of Butte Mountain. It was waxing that night, but my heart was waning.

Captain James Douglass passed away in my arms on November 13, 2005, at 8:30 pm. It was one hour after I had arrived at the hospital. It was twelve years to the day that I had received my wings.

CROSSING OVER

*S*ilence had become a familiar tone. It was the quiet that followed the wind. Just as an abrupt halt at the end of a squall, there is the unequivocal drop at the edge of an abyss. Each of us has been there. I envied the birds that could soar over the boundaries beneath them. They would not lead to an end, but to a new horizon. For they are not held to the ground as we are.

I reflected on my third marriage. I had married an airline captain who turned out to be verbally abusive and had serious anger issues. Captain Douglass had given me away at that ceremony. My father said, "I would give you away, but you just keep coming back!" So, I asked my Captain to be in my wedding. He didn't have any daughters, and I thought he would enjoy that. Afterwards, he had told my parents, "If I had my way, I would marry her... not give her away!" They had a good chuckle with that.

On the other hand, I wondered if he had really felt that way. He was a gentleman, and chivalry had been his unmistakable virtue. I had retained a love in my heart for Elio and Captain Douglass snuggled in next to him. Neither knew each other, and neither would. I never shook the thoughts of leaving; seemingly they reappeared over and over in my life.

After Jim's passing, stillness followed. I recall walking out of the hospital and stopping just outside the sliding doors. I hadn't moved forward enough, so the automatic doors continued to open and shut behind me. I heard nothing but the distant sounds of vehicles on the small two-lane highway, and if you traveled east, it led to the Sierra Nevada Mountains. If you traveled west, it would lead to San Francisco. I stood somewhere in the middle of my past and my future. It seemed my unmistakable virtue was making bad choices. The only actual choice I could hold on to were my two beautiful daughters.

I walked to my car uneasily. I hunkered into my red Dodge Neon SRT-4, fired up the engine, and pushed in the clutch, moving the shifter into first gear. I knew if Jim had recovered, he would have wanted to drive this. I reached over and switched on my windshield wipers. The remaining droplets were pushed aside and removed from existence. I drove out of the parking lot and headed for home.

Bianca and Katie were fast asleep when I arrived. I was surrounded by a numb intensity as I climbed the stairs to my bedroom. Bianca awoke and asked about Jim. I gave her the bad news, and she cried. I held her for a very long time before sending her back to bed. No words were spoken.

We were living in a two-story home I had purchased. It was nestled in town and not far from the old main street in Jackson. I was hired on at a local car dealership as their office manager. It was a family owned and operated dealership. I had been working the past ten years there and was able to support us with my income. Along with my employment, I was given a demo to drive, and this enabled me to drive many makes and models. That was the fun part of my job. The hours were grueling most of the time, but I was determined to be independent and free from constraints.

I had gotten myself ready for bed, turned off the lights and settled into my comfortable queen-size tranquility. I glanced around the room, admiring the photos that hung on the wall. My daughter's black and white poses from childhood were matted and framed in matching oak. I fixated on the photo of Jim and I as we walked down the aisle–my arm through his.

He was gone, and all I could think of was how much I would miss him. My eyes grew heavy, and I glanced at the clock on my bedside table. It was midnight, and I fell into a deep sleep.

My father gifted me his Cuckoo-clock, which sounded from the bottom of the stairs in a unified chorus with the mantel clock's resonating low-pitched tone. My sleepiness counted to three, and I slowly opened my eyes. My eyes were cloudy, and I struggled to clear my vision.

A man stood at the foot of my bed. His hair was gray, he wore a flannel shirt, and had a pencil mustache. His blue eyes sparkled with a familiar gleam. My eyes opened wide, and I sat up with a jolt. My heart beat rapidly and my breath was taken. I remember letting out a silent scream, and just as Captain Douglass had lost the fish on the end of his line, the vision was gone.

I had sat completely still and placed my hands over my heart. It felt as though I was having a heart attack, as my vital organ pounded its way out of my chest. For a moment, I remember thinking that I was about to follow him in death. I looked around the room in a panic and realized I was alone again. As I slowed my breathing and waited for my heart to stop palpitating, I whispered, "Jesus Christ, Jim. You almost gave me a heart attack!" The motion picture reel in my head rotated around and around. I recounted the events of the evening and I knew. I knew Captain Douglass was checking in on me, and I knew I had to let him go.

HIGH EXPECTATIONS

*W*hen I stood on the sands of the San Francisco Bay, I watched as the waves came in and broke along the shoreline. A stillness followed each break, and then I watched as they receded into the deep waters. It was a motion one could always expect, and an expectation that never failed.

HIGH EXPECTATIONS WILL ALWAYS LEAD TO DISAPPOINTMENT, AND YOU get exactly what you deserve. That was something a counselor said during a session in January 1994. Alex and I had been in counseling for weeks, and we were getting nowhere. The more we talked about our feelings, the more we grew apart. In the end, our counselor of supreme wisdom suggested I move out and leave the children with Alex. She felt they should not be taken from the only home they knew. She recommended I stay with my parents for a few days, and then settle on a place to live should I decide to leave with certainty.

It was upsetting to think that I was the one who should depart and not Alex. I struggled throughout the remainder of the day and proceeded with her advice. I packed a small suitcase and waited for Alex to come home. The girls were still quite young. Bella was seven and Bianca was four. I prepared our usual dinner and as we sat around the table; I waited for the right moment. It appeared time stood still. The dishes had been washed, and dessert was served, nevertheless, I could not find my words.

It was Alex who finally spoke up. He looked at Bella and Bianca and announced, "Mommy is leaving us tonight because she doesn't love us anymore!"

I gasped, and I stood up, wanting to punch him. Instead, I protested, "That isn't true. I love you two very much. I am not leaving you. I am taking a time out and visiting Grandma and Grandpa for a few days. Your dad and I felt it would be better if you stayed with him. This is your home, and I don't want to take you from it. I will be back, I promise."

Bella and Bianca ran to my arms. I began crying; they were crying, and I remember looking over at Alex, and he was crying too. This wasn't what I expected, and it definitely led to a great disappointment. I got exactly what I deserved. My hatred toward Alex and his harmful words were forever branded into my soul.

I regained my composure, walked to the back door, picked up my suitcase, turned and left. I don't recall the drive to my parents' house. My heart was torn, and my reasons for leaving seemed justifiable, yet I remained uncertain. The infinite wisdom of our marriage counselor did not seem to favor me in any form.

When I had arrived at the cabin in the mountains, I pulled up in front and watched the smoke as it rose from the chimney. The familiar water wheel turned alongside the steps leading to their front door. I had hoped my parents would help me in my separation from Alex. They were not aware of any problems, and I had never shared them. It was an unexpected visit, and I approached their home with caution.

I entered their front door as they both sat glued to the television set. It was early evening, and I surprised them when I announced myself. My father had given me the once-over and noticed my suitcase in hand. "What is going on, Tess?" he questioned.

"I am leaving Alex, and our counselor suggested it would be better if I stayed with you for a few days." My mother was doing her usual crocheting and continued with intensity. My father stood, raging with anger. He began his rant, and the feud was on.

"You can't leave Alex. You are making the biggest mistake of your life. What could you be thinking? He is a good father and husband."

I countered, "He lies about where he goes and what he is up to. It is common gossip that he plays house up and down the highway. I am tired of being his consolation prize. I thought his cheating would stop when we were married. What an idiot I was to have thought that. You are the one who encouraged me to marry him. I cannot be like my mother. She puts up with you and for that I view her as a saint. But me? I am not her. I will never be like her!" I glanced toward my mother, but she never looked up from her crocheting. "I want to be the one he comes home to and loves. I am his wife, and yet I am as lonely as when I wasn't. He hides pornography from me and thinks I am totally unaware of his fetish."

My father and I had inched in closer, nose to nose. His face was red with fury. "You will never make a man happy, Tess, and you know why? It's because you do not know how to serve. Go ahead and live your life of misery. The children don't deserve this, and you are going to hurt everyone else in the process. I am ashamed of you!"

That's when I lost it. I realized my parents were not going to support my separation. I blurted out, "You are right, I will never make a man happy. I am going to be with a woman. I am going to become a homosexual!"

I glanced at my mother as she sat on the couch. Her crochet needle working at warp speed. Her words, "Oh my, oh my, oh my."

I picked up my suitcase and headed for the front door. My father grabbed my shoulder, trying to stop me. "I'm sorry I came here. I won't bother you anymore," I said and pushed his hand away.

"Love means never having to say you're sorry," Father said and smiled. I rolled my eyes in disgust and walked away.

"What a crock" I responded.

I threw my suitcase in the car and drove back down the highway. It was a miserable drive. I remember thinking this wasn't the way to handle things. Our counselor was grossly mistaken, and I could not imagine a life separated from my children. Alex did not love me.

I was embarrassing him in this quaint community. I was embarrassing my father. It was all about them, and I immediately pulled up in front of the flagpole, sitting at the entrance to the airport. The flag was illuminated by the mounted flood light. The flag rippled in the breeze. I shut off my car and reflected on my actions.

I turned the idea of a divorce around and around in my head. The courts would see this as a form of desertion, and I would never gain custody of my daughters. I stared at the rows and rows of airplanes, started up my car, and drove over to my hanger. I opened up the door and walked to my airplane. It had been three months since I received my wings. It was the most wonderful day of my life, aside from giving birth to Bella and Bianca.

I jumped into the cockpit and glanced at the instrument panel. I recall wondering if aviation was really that important to me and could I manage a single mother's life, career, and continue to fly? Could I afford the luxury that aviation costs? Was staying with Alex a good enough reason because he took care of me financially? Was I with him only for the money? Was my father correct? Would I ever make a man happy? I thought of Captain Douglass's words of wisdom, "It is better to live a life alone, than to live your life with the wrong person."

I rendered deep thoughts about a recent weighty encounter.

I was buying groceries at a popular small market, and I ran into Julia. She asked me, "How are you doing, Tess? Rumor has it that you and Alex are not doing so well?"

My response was sincere, "We are struggling, and he doesn't want me to leave with my children. So, we are in counseling. How are you and Jasta? We stopped hanging out with you and I never understood why?"

She seemed uneasy with my question. Her posture went rigid, and she cleared her throat. Her response lingered in my head, "Well, I have quite the story for you, Tess. This isn't the time or place; however, when you are ready to hear it, give me a call. I am certain, what I have to say will guarantee you custody!"

I raised an eyebrow, gave her my Katie look, and then smiled. With a nod of my head, I walked away thinking it was probably another affair that Alex was having. How many of those did I need to hear about? At that moment I shrugged it off, just like I did with all subjects about Alex's infidelities.

The instrument panel came back into view. I had contemplated going for a flight, but the tears began to flow, and I thought about navigating at night in this state of mind. The captain in me said, no. I decidedly buttoned up the airplane, closed the hanger door, and returned to my car. I drove the winding road home and pulled into the garage.

The house was dark, and I struggled to get the key in the back door keyhole. I walked into the dark kitchen and turned on a light. The house was eerily silent, and I tip-toed to the children's rooms. They were asleep, and I gazed at their innocence. Children are angelic while sleeping, and I leaned over and gently kissed each of their cheeks.

I undressed and gently slid into bed alongside Alex. He woke and sat up. "What are you doing, Tess? You came back?" he questioned.

"Yes, I came back. I am not leaving without my children. I will stay and try to get along with you, but no one is going to make me leave this house alone, not you and certainly not that idiot counselor we have been seeing."

Alex drew me in, and for the first time in our marriage, he wept. He wept harder than when I turned down his proposal. He turned and buried his head in his pillow and sobbed, "This is my payback for all the hurt I have caused you. I have been an ass, and in the process, I have lost you."

I remained silent while the sympathy in me wanted to reassure him that I would stay forever. He wrenched at my guilt and I felt horrible for hurting Alex, but most of all for hurting my daughters. I thought about his words and wondered if he was sincere. All I ever wanted was to be loved. I wanted to be held, and even at this critical moment of our marriage, he turned his back to me. I squinted my eyes and stared at the glowing streetlamp. That was when I prayed for a sign. I needed something, or someone, to lead me. I was incapable of making a decision, so I had decided not to. I would stay and I would live each day waiting… waiting for a sign.

A DARK TRUTH

$\mathcal{W}$ith a reservation resting in my heart, I had listened with uncertainty as her phone rang. Jasta answered, and he seemed to have sensed why I was calling. He did not hesitate to hand off the phone to Julia. I braced myself for another ugly story about Alex, but I was driven by curiosity. "Hey, Tess. That didn't take you long?" Julia broke in.

My response was that of a quivering puppy with its tail between its legs, "I'm dying to hear about whatever story you have to share about Alex."

Julia continued, "I would prefer to speak with you in person. How about we meet at the park in Sutter Creek? Bring your daughters, and I'll bring mine. You haven't seen our newest edition yet!"

Jasta and Julia had welcomed in the arrival of a baby girl. She was born just a few months prior, and I had neglected to ask what they named her, or ask how the baby was doing, or ask how Julia was recovering? It dawned on me; I may have come across as insensitive.

I made certain to arrive at the park with a baby gift in hand. Bella and Bianca ran ahead towards the swing-sets. I glanced down at my watch and noted we were early. I took advantage of the time and helped the girls onto the swings. Julia's oldest daughter, Vanessa–from a previous marriage, shared Bella's age. It wasn't long before Julia arrived. Vanessa made a mad dash toward the merry-go-round and my daughters insisted on joining her. As they began running to the other playground equipment, Julia introduced me to her baby. She was tiny in her infant carrier, and I was taken back by her beautiful red hair. We took a seat at the picnic table, which allowed a direct view of our children at play.

Julia spoke up first, "This is Scarlett, the newest member of our family!"

I looked at her with my usual examining eye. "She has red hair, just like Bella! Can you imagine that? Both Jasta and Alex have a red-headed daughter! What are the odds of that? She is beautiful, and she is so tiny. Can I hold her?" I asked.

"Yes, you can hold her," Julia responded.

I took Scarlett into my arms and cradled her while she cooed, and I noticed her delicate smile and small fingers. I drew in her scent and it brought back memories of my own daughters when they were newborns. I closed my eyes while holding her, and for a moment I had forgotten why I was there. The innocence gently enfolded us, just as a veil covers a respectable woman. She was a delicate flower, waiting to unfold and inhale the life ahead of her.

I placed Scarlett back into her infant carrier and turned to Julia, "So, let's get to it, shall we? What in the world could you possibly have to tell me I haven't already heard?" I waited in anticipation of a wild affair, or numerous ones. Julia drew in a deep breath and spewed her story.

The construction of the invisible wall that had formed between us was finally explained. It began during our Friday night dates from racquetball to Mexican food. As we ate our dinner at our usual booth, Alex would move his arm underneath the table and place his hand on Julia's knee and squeeze it. He would inch his hand up her inner thigh until his hand met hers, and she would stop him. Not long afterwards, he began calling her while Jasta was at work. It began with small conversations; all the while, Alex was gathering information about Jasta's work schedule. Soon, Alex confessed his attraction to Julia. He admitted his desire to have a secret affair with her. The phone calls grew in intensity, bordering on harassment. Alex continued to pursue her, even though she told him (over and over) that she was not interested.

My mind became paralyzed. I could hear her words, but a buzzing sound grew in intensity between my ears. Her voice slowly moved over my realization, just as a cloud slowly progresses around an airplane's wing. Her story was not just another love affair, or about someone I didn't know, it was about her and my husband.

I interrupted, "You mean, this is about you and Alex? Alex was pursuing you?"

"Yes, and there is more," she answered.

Alex and Bianca commonly took drives to Sutter Creek on Saturday mornings. Bella would stay home with me. Bianca loved spending one-on-one time with her dad. It was a good time for them to bond. Bella loved our one-on-one time without Bianca. It was like the old times before Bianca was born. Bella and I would play a game or watch a favorite Disney cartoon. Sometimes Bella would wash the breakfast dishes with me. She would push a kitchen chair up to the sink and fill up the dishpan with sudsy water.

It was during one of those innocent Saturday mornings that Alex and Bianca took their drive; only this time, they took a detour to Jasta and Julia's home. They had a secluded ranch on the outskirts of Drytown. Julia had waved goodbye to Jasta as he left early that morning to post up in a nearby prison guard tower. He wore his badge and uniform proudly–his gun holstered by his side. Minutes had turned into hours and Julia heard a car approach their home. She watched as our pickup truck parked outside their entrance. Alex carried Bianca to the front door and rang their doorbell. Julia, still in her bathrobe, hesitated to open the door. Alex had progressed from ringing the bell to pounding on the door.

Julia maintained a cool demeanor while sharing her horror story. My jaw continued to fall open, and my eyes watered with embarrassment. She proceeded with intensity.

Alex and Bianca entered her home. He was persistent, and as he put Bianca down, he instructed her to go play with Vanessa. The two girls were delighted to see each other and ran off to Vanessa's room. Alex walked over and closed the bedroom door and turned toward Julia. Julia said she flushed with panic. Alex coaxed her into the master bedroom.

"Did you and Alex have sex?" I asked.

"Let me put it this way, Tess," she responded. "Now I know what it is like to be date raped. This happened while Jasta and I were trying to have a baby. We were not having any success, and it may not be a coincidence that we both have red-headed daughters."

I was not only paralyzed, embarrassed, shocked, and mortified... I was ashamed. I was ashamed to discover that my husband paraded around this small town, in that fashion. I was ashamed to have his name, be his wife and most of all... be that oblivious. I had surrounded myself with brilliant minds, family, and friends who encouraged me to marry Alex, and I had listened.

All I could do, that innocent day in that innocent park with that innocent newborn baby, was sob. I looked at her tiny countenance again and realized she could be Bella and Bianca's sister. This was not even close to any expectation I had when I agreed to meet with Julia. What I got was definitely not what I deserved.

Julia continued, much like the bricklayer who stacks his blocks between each layer of mortar, trowel in hand. After Alex and Bianca left, she was beyond upset. She waited for Jasta to arrive home. Jasta bounced in with his usual delightful unsuspecting demeanor. It soon became obvious to Jasta of Julia's distress. She was distraught, and when Jasta pushed for information, she broke. She spilled the event, like flood waters filling up the adjacent creek. Jasta was furious. He grabbed his gun, headed to his truck, and sped out of their driveway. Julia grabbed Vanessa and tried to catch up with Jasta in her car. She pulled him over to the side of the road.

"I insisted to Jasta I needed a husband who worked at the prison, not a convicted felon to visit. He isn't worth it," she continued. Jasta had every intention of shooting Alex; he was that enraged. Julia calmed him down, somewhat, and convinced him to return home. It was then that Jasta and Julia stopped associating with us. Not long afterwards, she was pregnant.

"So, you see, Tess. If the courts will not grant you custody, I will go to court and testify that you should have the girls and not Alex. I will confess everything. Jasta is one hundred percent behind me."

I dropped my head onto Julia's shoulder. All I could say was, "I am so sorry, Julia. I am so sorry. I am sorry that my husband did that to you. I am so sorry!"

Bella, Bianca, and Vanessa huddled around us. I remember feeling their little hands patting me on my back and their voices repeating, "It's okay, Mommy. Please don't cry."

We returned home, the three white birds on that swaying branch. It became apparent to me the wind had kicked up. I would not be alone when I made that leap of faith. I had prayed for a sign... and I most certainly received one.

AIR FORCE ONE

$\mathcal{I}$t was October 3, 1993, when I flew with Captain Douglass on a VOR (Very High Frequency Omnidirectional Range) training flight. It was a tough part of my syllabus but none the less, very important to understand and execute. On that day, our 42nd President William Jefferson Clinton was flying into California and visiting McClellan Airforce base. When I received a NOTAM (Notice to Airmen) alerting us of the restricted airspace, I immediately re-routed our flight to bypass the President's itinerary. It was not uncommon for unrestricted airspace to become restricted because of the high volume of air bases in California. That day was no different.

We departed Red Bluff airport and were clear of the tower frequency, and we dialed in and monitored the inbound flight for Air Force One. Aside from the instructions Air Force One was receiving, it seemed a silent flight. Air Force One was beginning its step-down instructions on their long final approach into McClellan. As we continued listening, we both heard an alert given to the Air Force One Captain, "Air Force One, you have traffic twelve o'clock, same altitude, five miles."

It didn't sink in until Captain Douglass looked over at me and said, "That's us, Babe. I'll take the controls!" Captain sat up with intensity and banked a hard left turn. As I scanned the surrounding area, a large Air Force One approached and banked left as well. It all happened so fast, and both my Captain and President Clinton's Captain turned their aircraft in the opposite direction of protocol for a head on collision. Training instructs each aircraft bank right, yet when Captain Douglass spotted the oncoming jet, he immediately cleared the way regardless of the rule.

As I observed Airforce One pass by our right-wing, I waved to them. We were so close, and yet we weren't. It seemed we moved in slow motion as the jet meandered by. The presidential seal was positioned on the fuselage, and the painted American flag trailed on its tail. I was in awe, and then I noticed the nervousness from my Captain. "Let's get on the ground. We were too close, and we may be in trouble."

I took over flying my Cessna 152 and descended into Auburn Airport. Once on the ground, Captain and I sat and shared a soda. It was a pleasantly comfortable day. As we discussed our Air Force One encounter, it was alarming to me that President Clinton was not in the restricted airspace, nor was he arriving during the timeframe of our NOTAM.

It was later reported that U.S. special forces stormed a compound in Somalia that same day in October. It was a failed operation, also known as Black Hawk Down. We lost nineteen U.S. soldiers and seventy-three were wounded. Perhaps President Clinton was in Air Force One at his command center, and it was with good reason he was not anywhere near the sky's expectation. Our Air Force One encounter was the least of his concerns, and my guess is, he wasn't aware of the situation, having more critical issues at hand.

I certainly did not expect an Air Force One encounter when I began my flight that day. Our pilots, in those two black hawk helicopters, did not expect to be shot down by Somalia forces. I was fortunate. Unfortunately, our soldiers were not. While fighting lasted through the night, it was not an expectation to see our murdered soldiers being drug through the streets in Somalia on T.V. Eventually our troops were rescued, and in time, all the dead were returned home.

It became one of President Clinton's critical errors he made during his presidency. The unsuccessful operation led to another bad decision, made by him six months later–decidedly to remain neutral in the Rwandan genocide. Rwanda claimed over one million people had perished during the genocide massacre. Our soldiers were not there to help them. It seems even a President can make a poor decision while surrounded by secret intelligence and brilliant minds. At the end of the day, we are all human and somehow that eased my reality.

We returned to our home base in Jackson that afternoon. I parked my airplane in the hanger and secured the doors. Captain drove off in his Karmann Ghia, and I walked over to the Benz. I noticed Jasta driving up and parking alongside his hanger. He glanced my way and then turned away as though he didn't see me. I could not help but wonder... what did I do to him that made him dislike me so?

I shrugged it off, like so many things. My mind was fixed on the encounter of the day. Looking back on October 3, 1993, I was in my own little bubble. Lives were lost and horrific tortures carried out across the seas at faraway lands. I glanced at the American flag as I drove away from the little airport in Jackson, California. It wasn't as small as Niksic, nor did we have a *one strip grass runway*. World War II was far behind us. Our flag stood with pride, and once again I felt incredibly lucky. My difficulties and struggles seemed so small in humanity's dispersion of life.

On a scale between extreme and opposite points, I had navigated through its depths and I was unaware of what was to come.

AN AWAKENING

"*J*ust because someone wrote it, or someone said it, doesn't make it true." Those were the words from Captain Douglass as we sat on an outdoor dining patio during lunch. The air was warm for February. I shared the entire story with him, and he sat listening while letting out deep sighs through his mouth, revealing disappointment in his eyes.

"Are those supposed to be words of encouragement?" I asked.

"No, not at all. I believe her story; Julia, right? I believe she would not have suggested a possible sibling to your daughters, had it not been true. On the other hand, there are always two sides to a story. You may want to confront Alex and see what he has to say, before deciding to leave him."

"What about all the other affairs, and the lies? Am I supposed to just accept them as part of life? As part of marriage? Is that what *Till-Death-Do-You-Part* means? Am I to live forever and ever with a man who is unfaithful?" I blurted out.

"Babe, do you know how smart you are? Have you any idea how beautiful you are? By the way, you look great in black! You can do anything if you put your mind to it. You don't have to do anything if you don't want to. You are in charge of your life, and now *that* life includes your daughters. In their eyes, you will become the ideal of what a woman should look and act like. Show your strength, say your words, and make your decision based on knowledge. Knowledge is powerful, and truth will never change. You are an independent person, and with that, challenges are inevitable. Your daughters will grow up seeing you as living a lie, or living the truth. They will be women one day, and when they look back, it will be through the eyes of an adult. Right now, they can only react from emotion because the truth would be impossible for them to comprehend. Be gentle, Babe, and love them. As long as you have them in your life, you will never be alone," Captain reiterated.

THAT WAS A CONVERSATION I WOULD NEVER FORGET. "WORDS OF wisdom," I whispered as I stood in the small airport office of Westover Field. I fixed my eyes on the large portrait hanging of Captain Douglass, posing in his flight jumpsuit with his fishing pole in hand. I had taken that picture in Hope Valley. Captain was teaching me how to spin fish in the chilly waters of Carson River.

When the memorial service was held, I had given his family the most recent photo I had. They liked it so much; it was enlarged and placed on an easel. Tumble weeds crossed the familiar tarmac at Calaveras Maury Rasmussen Field, while people gathered in a nearby hanger. Many pairs of red socks sat in a welcoming basket, along with programs of memorable pictures taken during his flying career.

"Red socks," I said as I took a pair for myself. He always wore red socks, no matter his attire.

When I questioned him, his reply was, "I have four sons who were always taking my socks. When I figured it out, I began wearing red socks. They would never take those. After that, it became my signature."

I took his red socks and took a seat alongside other fellow pilots whom Captain Douglass had been acquainted.

One by one, family and friends shared their stories. I listened with a heavy heart, and an open mind at the wonderful tales, adventures, and mishaps. My Captain had lived an incredible life, and I was incredibly blessed to have shared a small piece of that with him. I mustered up the courage to speak and made my slow walk toward the podium. I thought long and hard before speaking, smoothing my hands down the sides of my black dress. I could not bring myself to share his last hour, it was too painful. So, I shared the banana story. It was received with a common recognition, and it brought a big laugh to all present.

His family gestured warmth and gratitude for the comfort I had provided him in his last hour. I was presented with his portrait as I left. I shared his image with the small airport where we first officially met. I had the photo framed in gold with an inscribed brass plate, his official rank, name, his birthdate, and date of his death.

As I left the small café, I gave Captain a final hug. "Thank you for always listening and for your words of advice!" He smiled with that twinkle in his eyes, "Happy Birthday, Babe. I know you will do the right thing."

I drove home to relieve Allie of her babysitting duties. I continued to be uncertain as to the validity of Julia's story. I knew in my heart that Alex would deny it, and that would bring doubt to my mind. I felt there was more to it than what she confessed to me, and perhaps what she confessed to Jasta. The truth will eventually surface, and in that moment, I had decided it didn't matter.

The next day, I moved the girls and me into a condominium in Jackson. It was small, but we needed small. I purchased twin beds and a small dresser for their room. I used cardboard boxes for my clothes and a spare double bed that Alex and I had for my room. The complex had a swimming pool, Jacuzzi, and game room. This alone was exciting to the girls, and I was happy they could see a positive light despite the separation from their dad.

I waited a few months before confronting Alex. It happened one day when he drove over to pick up the girls for a weekend visitation. They were upstairs, getting dressed when he arrived. We were downstairs, talking in the kitchen. Alex made a sarcastic remark, "You know, Tess. You are the most selfish person I have ever known. All you think about is yourself. You are hurting our children, and this will have an effect on them throughout their entire life. I don't care if you love me or not, but you will regret this one day. Just wait and see."

I lost it, as I did so many other times. I couldn't hold back and contain myself any longer. I blurted out, "I know about you and Julia. I know what happened at their ranch house while Jasta was at work. You actually took our daughter with you? You stand in judgment of me, and you were my husband. How could you do that to me, to us?"

His eyes had flickered from brown to white while rapidly blinking. Then his face turned red, and the wannabe defensive linebacker, wishful-thinking, stat-keeper, came out in him. "I don't know what she told you, but it was a lie. By the way, she grabbed my crotch first!"

I could hardly believe my ears. He was admitting to it and denying it in the same breath. My volume increased, "I don't care who grabbed who first, you were my husband, and you were behaving that way. You were calling her and playing patty-cake under the table when we had dinner with them. You disgust me, and I want you out! Leave now!"

Our nose-to-nose battle had grown with such intensity that neither of us noticed the two girls had emerged from upstairs. Bella began to howl and ran out the front door. Bianca was crying, and Alex immediately picked her up. "Look what you've done!" he yelled at me.

I bolted out the front door and found Bella on the sidewalk near the parking area. She was crouched down and crying hysterically. I picked her up and cradled her. I tried to comfort her, but Alex emerged and ordered her to leave with him. He ushered two crying girls to his truck, buckled them in, looked back at me with a glare, and drove away.

I collapsed on the kitchen floor. Images of Bella and Bianca falling off that broken branch haunted me. I had no idea how much the children had heard.

As I laid on the floor, it dawned on me… I never did mention Scarlett. Alex didn't know that little detail. He didn't deserve to know. That little detail would grow into a woman one day, and she did not need to be a part of our fucked-up life.

I WALKED OVER TO CAPTAIN DOUGLASS'S PORTRAIT AND LAID MY PALM ON his image. I stood motionless and silent. "Hey, Tess!" I heard.

I slowly turned around and there stood Jasta.

SMALL TOWN

*I*n time, Father and I mended our bridges. He finally succumbed to the realization that I was nothing like my mother. I was born with freedom in my heart and an independence instilled within me, which probably originated from his time in prison.

I endured older siblings who were not always kind, and an older brother who pushed me around way too often. I had learned from an early age to sink or swim; or in my case, fall or fly. My running shoes that graced the sands of the San Leandro's bird sanctuary trails were replaced with soft toed shoes that could feel the pads of the rudder pedals beneath my feet. It was with every free moment I would find myself at the local airport, and when I flew alone, I found my incandescent latitude. I finally had something that I could hold on to, something I earned all by myself, and something no one could ever take away from me—not in a divorce, not on a dark night without security or presence of mind, and not on a paper covered examination table while staring at a cold concrete ceiling.

After much coaxing (and guilt playing on my part), Father agreed to go flying with me. The Shasta Fire in California had created poor visibility for the navigator that year. He observed me with a close eye as I went through my pre-flight inspection. He reminded me to observe this or that and be careful of this or be careful of that. We boarded the plane, and while I buckled him in, I noticed the small beads of sweat forming on his brow. He was very nervous, and for the first time with him I was the pilot in command. Unfortunately, my father was diagnosed with macular degeneration, causing his vision to deteriorate over the years. He seemed more nervous about his inability to fly the plane (should we have an emergency), and even more nervous about my capability to handle one.

We departed from runway 19 on a straight-out departure. I climbed above the small town of Jackson and then banked west toward the San Joaquin Valley. Father rubbed his hands together nervously and struggled to make out the terrain below. I pointed out the scenic areas of Butte Mountain, Camanche Lake Reservoir, the small lakes in the distance, and Mount Diablo in the west. He seemed pleased, but it became apparent to me that my father was out of his comfort zone. When I suggested he take hold of the control wheel, he declined. His love for flying was still within his heart, but his body was failing and along with it, his wings.

I looped over the town of Sutter Creek and followed Highway 49 toward Drytown and Amador City. I continued pointing out reference points, but Father remained quiet. It was an unfamiliar stillness. My father was boastful and loud, and always in control. He wasn't one to allow a woman to be in charge, and now he was at the mercy of his baby daughter; the same daughter who wanted to fly and was told that women do not fly. The advice was offered to the wrong daughter. I pulled back from him when he reiterated, "You will never make a man happy." I snickered at the thought. He was correct, and I wasn't making him happy at that moment.

I announced our inbound position to Westover Field. Father seemed relieved when we entered the traffic pattern. I cautiously executed each approach and focused on the runway, as my Captain had always instructed. I descended gracefully and with ease. We settled onto the asphalt with a delicate squeak. Father let out a sigh of recognition, followed by a gleam on his face. We smiled at each other, both of us sharing our dimples, "Nice landing, Tess."

THAT WAS THE ONLY TIME MY FATHER FLEW WITH ME. HE PASSED AWAY A few years after Captain Douglass. It was fast, and without pain. I continued to stare at the memorial photograph in the small airport office. I wished I could see both of them one more time... *one more time* I hushed. My train of thought was interrupted, "Tess?"

Jasta had a big smile on his face. "How are you doing?" he mumbled as he swayed back and forth. His green cargo pants, leather flight jacket, and combat boots reminded me of a Rambo movie. He stood tall and resembled Clint Eastwood.

"I'm okay," my mind raced with questions.

"I would love to chat with you. How about we sit on the wooden bench outside and talk? It's been so long, and so much has changed," he said with insistence.

Jasta and I talked for hours, and then we took a stroll over to his hanger. He had built a white RV-4 experimental airplane. His hanger had an area set up like a living room, featuring a couch, coffee table, chairs, and television. He turned on his AM/FM radio and opened a small refrigerator, retrieving a couple beers.

"So, Jasta. How is Julia?" I quizzed.

"We split up. And I am now going through a divorce. I caught her fooling around with a local pilot here at our airport. She moved out and moved in with him," he continued looking down as though he was embarrassed.

"Really? That makes me wonder how true her story was about her and Alex? Care to discuss that with me? I have contemplated a mutual affair between those two, but I haven't any grounds to prove it, unless you do?"

His eyes met mine, and I could see his pupils had dilated. His face flushed. It became silent in the hanger, and I waited for an answer. "Tell me your story, Tess, and then I will tell you mine."

I told the story again; the way Julia had told me. He listened with a nod here and there. I tried to give as much detail as she had. He listened without any interruptions until I finished. I waited in anticipation of his response.

"Yep, that about sums it up!" he answered.

"Wait, so you agree? Do you agree there is a possibility that Scarlett could be a sister to Bella and Bianca?"

He pursed his lips, ran his hand through his sandy blonde hair and nodded. "She is my daughter. I will always see her that way. We don't know for certainty. Only a DNA test can prove that. No one can change the fact that I am her legal father. Not even an asshole like Alex. I felt sorry for you, Tess. You did not deserve to be treated that way. Julia and I vowed never to mingle with either of you to save our sanity and our marriage. So much for the marriage part. I sometimes wonder myself if it was a mutual affair, rather than a date rape, as she claimed. We will never really know. Now that she has left me for another man, it makes me wonder."

I struggled with adjectives, just as people struggle with words, concepts, or visions. I read that Ernest Hemingway distrusted certain adjectives, which led him to distrust certain people. I could relate.

I could see Jasta's pain and humiliation in his tormented green eyes. It seemed we were two birds with broken feathers. He stood up and walked to the hanger door and closed it. I watched as he turned and approached me with a tenderness that I had never noticed before. He reached for my hand and helped me up. The soft music played in the background, and he danced with me. He drew me in close and there was an electrical surge between us. I could feel his breath in my ear and his fingertips pulsated against mine.

"Tess," he whispered, "I really care about you. I find you captivating."

For some strange reason, this felt right. He felt good, and yet I had never thought of him in this way. I felt a need, but then I hesitated. This was really strange. We were in a small town, and a small town will talk. What would people think? My mind spun with worry. He drew me in tight against his body and then released me.

"Let's go to dinner, Tess. How about Mexican?" he said with a wink.

"That sounds perfect!" I was relieved.

During our meal, we caught up on so much of our lives. Jasta talked about the inmates on his watch, and I shared stories of the auto industry world. We continued our banter until closing; one by one we watched each patron leave the restaurant.

Jasta drove a tidy old pickup truck. He was a simple man, creative and excellent with his wood working craftsmanship. We bounced over divots in the asphalt until arriving at my car. He lingered, "How about going for a night flight tomorrow? We could fly over to Columbia and have dinner?" he asked. "Or..." he hesitated, "I could have you over to my place, and I will cook for you?"

"I love a home cooked meal," I was eager to be alone with him. I suddenly wanted him, and I wanted him soon.

The following evening, I cautiously arrived at his ranch style home. I hadn't been to his place since he and Cheryl (his first wife) were married. The two of them built this home, and when they separated, she hated the seclusion it provided and decidedly moved into town. Julia moved in, and Alex had his way with her here. I slowly pulled up in front, parked, and sat idle while imagining Alex doing the same. I had to shake off the memory and convince myself that was then, and it was not my fault. I should have run. Instead, I walked to his front door and knocked.

Jasta bounced to the door with a big smile. "Come in, come in!" I heard Fleetwood Mac playing "Everywhere" in the background. Jasta had prepared a nice salad, baked potatoes, and had fired up the BBQ. He was marinating a couple nice steaks and had opened a bottle of California's Vino Noceto's Sangiovese; a wonderful selection from his wine cellar. He was charismatic with much enthusiasm. He appeared enchanted at my arrival, and I was eagerly impressed with his talents. Jasta was nothing like I had imagined. He was quite the opposite of all the derogatory remarks Alex had made about him. It was obvious to me why. Alex didn't hold a candle to him.

As the sun set, the temperature dropped. Jasta built a fire in the fireplace, and we settled into a quiet evening of after-dinner conversation. We had polished off two bottles of wine, and I was no longer in any condition to drive. With very little persuasion, Jasta whisked me up into his arms and carried me to his daughter Lilly's room. Lilly was away at college, and he had built a beautiful rustic twin bed for her. When I collapsed on top of the patchwork quilt, Jasta gently covered me with a blanket. He kissed my cheek as lightly as a feather and whispered, "Good night, Tess."

I had sensed his presence in the doorway, and I had a sense of security. This was not the room the incident occurred in, and I had no sense of any negativity within its walls. I had felt protected, not just because a prison guard was watching over me—it was more than that. I was gradually moving further from Alex and closer to the truth.

I GO, YOU GO

Streams of morning light filtered through the curtain pleats that flowed over the window's ledge. I lifted my head and peered around Lilly's room. It was quiet in the house, and the smell of rustic wood wrapped around me comfortably. I wanted to leave without waking Jasta. I gathered together my personal items and tip-toed through the living room. Jasta slept on the couch with a blanket thrown over him. He stirred when I opened the front door.

My car meandered down the dirt road, which took me to the familiar highway in the Gold Country. My feelings for Jasta were trying their best to emerge, but the familiarity of another heartbreak outweighed the possibilities. I buried them, just as I had so many times before. I inhaled the escaping night air and turned the events around and around in my head.

Jasta was persistent. He called soon afterwards, and I had agreed to meet him at the airport for a scenic flight. His version of a scenic flight differed greatly from mine. Jasta was a well-trained aerobatic pilot, and his RV-4 was designed specifically for that.

Jasta helped me into the tight space seated directly behind him. We sat tandem with a clear bubble canopy above our heads. Jasta buckled me into the harness system. Each of my legs straddled his seat with a

239

rudder pedal mounted alongside, and I had a flight stick positioned between my legs (much like my control wheel). There was a throttle to my left, and all the instruments were in front of Jasta. We were squeezed in like two sardines in a tin can. I placed my headset on, and we made a standard radio check.

The RV-4 had conventional landing gear (two wheels forward of center of gravity and one under the tail fin). Jasta fired up the engine and hollered, "Clear!" Due to the lack of forward visibility, we taxied to the runway making slow movements to the right and then to the left. Jasta made his usual pre-flight run-up and cleared the area for inbound traffic. He rolled onto the runway and powered forward to lift the tail. Within seconds, we ascended into a steep climb. We circled over Lake Camanche and made a fast barrel roll over the prison. Jasta climbed to a higher altitude and began a loop. I was counting one through ten as we looped up, over the earths' surface. "More? Tess?" Jasta questioned over the intercom.

"No, I'm good," I grimaced, reminding myself how little I enjoyed roller coasters.

We headed back to Westover Field and entered the traffic pattern on a long final approach. Jasta had watched too much of the movie *Top Gun* in his spare time. I felt as though we were about to land on an aircraft carrier. He was low and fast and settled his ship right on the numbers. It was a perfect landing, and the total opposite of what mine always looked like.

We taxied back to his hanger and buttoned up the plane. We enjoyed a cold beer when suddenly Julia's car approached. She rolled down her car window and talked with Jasta, all the while glancing my way. She nodded at me but continued with the berating reprimands. She drove off with as much velocity and fury as she could muster. Jasta became three shades of red and remained quiet.

It was awkward, and I had felt it was time to go. I stood to leave. "Don't go, Tess. Stay and finish your beer. I'm feeling hungry and would love to grab a burger at Mel's. What do you say?" he measured me up, like someone who wanted a new pair of shoes.

"Ok, sounds good" the buster browns in me responded.

Over the course of six months, Jasta and I had become good friends. We began our relationship from the never-ending broken relationships in each of our lives. I am almost certain it could have become a wonderful union, but the Tess Hamilton in me wanted to run. I was riddled with feelings of betrayal to Jasta's first wife, Cheryl. When I ran into her at Lilly's college graduation ceremony, it was unpleasant, and I felt such uneasiness as Jasta held my hand.

I had grown up in a sea of people back in the San Francisco Bay Area. Some of which I would never know. Here in this small quaint county of Amador, it seemed everyone was connected by six-degrees of separation; Alex was the base while I had become the exponent. My daughters and I were the real numbers, while everyone else became an equation. Alex, Cheryl, and Julia fell into that equation, and for me it didn't add up.

Happiness appeared in short bursts of internal weakness. Jasta had tried his best to love me, but the real me was beyond his reach. I became his confusion, leading to excessive drinking and insecurity. It was always my own fault. I had lacked the communication skills needed for him.

I was the epitome of continuous restlessness. Even as I laid in a warm bath of bubbly lavender, Jasta read to me, *I Carry Your Heart With Me*, by E.E. Cummings. One would seemingly be transformed with this, along with our glowing long walks, his scenic flights, and plentiful candle lit dinners. It should have been enough to keep me there, but thoughts of leaving always reappeared.

BEFORE WE MEET AGAIN

$\mathcal{I}$ had planted an olive tree in my backyard in memory of my father and mother. She passed away two years after my father. Mother had become riddled with Alzheimer's disease, and during the final months of her life, she struggled to recognize me. Bella and Bianca would spend hours reading to her, and Bella's red hair would trigger some familiar memories. Soon, that drifted away too. When her final hours came, my sister Katie, Jessica, and I remained by her bedside. We had stayed late into the night and returned home to get some needed sleep. It was only a few hours later that I received the call she had passed away.

When we had reappeared in her hospital room, Katie and Jessica needed to leave the room while Mother was prepared for the funeral home. They dashed out to get us all a Starbucks coffee. I was the one who could not leave her. I wanted to be the one who bathed her and prepared her, not a stranger. I dressed her in a white gown afterwards and covered her with a white sheet.

Both my parents were cremated, and we held onto Father's ashes until Mother was gone. I stood watching, Katie by my side, as my mother's empty shell entered the crematorium. I had placed a bouquet of yellow roses in her folded hands. A tuff of her white hair extended through the handle opening as she rolled away.

It was a vision I will never forget and will always hold dear to my heart. I was blessed to accompany her through a transition, and I was blessed with Captain Douglass's as well. I walked away that day feeling empty and lost. Where does one go from there?

The fall leaves of October crushed underneath my footsteps. The light showers left their whiff of autumn. I waved goodbye to Katie and drove off in my car, meandering through the streets of Jackson.

I LEFT HOME EARLY ON THAT CRISP JANUARY MORNING IN 2011. I followed the highways, crossed the San Mateo Bridge, and exited to the Golden Gate National Cemetery. Fields of yellow mustard flowers stretched over the rolling hills. Willie Nelson's, "Angel Flying Too Close to the Ground" resonated from my CD player. I lowered my car window, and I was engulfed by the scent of succulent eucalyptus trees.

I entered the beautiful Golden Gates lined with rows of fallen heroes in perfect formation. My eyes followed the road to their resting place. The breeze washed through my hair as I exited my car. I took in the pungent oxygenated air. "Home," I whispered with a slight smile. Ahead, an old oak tree leaned over as if to say, "Come here, you have found us." I buttoned up my black wool coat and stepped with a respectful footing, while flashes of cowboy boots projected their image.

I paused at the white marble headstone etched with, "Donald J. Hamilton." My brother had been sleeping for so long, and alongside him rested my father and mother. They were finally together. I ran my index finger along the chiseled names; a jet airliner passed overhead. It reminded me of my youth and my wishful dreams.

I REMEMBERED FATHER USING AN OLD FASHION SHAVING MUG AND BRUSH. Early morning, I would sit on the edge of the bathtub and watch him lather up his face. The distant sounds of fog horns reminded me that the ocean was nearby. He would meticulously run his razor down his cheeks and under his chin, leaving a smooth trail as a snowplow does after a heavy snowfall. His hands would dip into the sink and retrieve warm water to splash on his face. His scent lingered from his Old Spice aftershave.

AND THEN MY MEMORIES CARRIED IN CAPTAIN DOUGLASS, FIGHTING FOR his fish just beyond the San Francisco Airport next to the cemetery. The coastal winds blew my long hair over my face, and as I raised a hand to move it, I saw them. Three blue birds had taken flight from the arms of the lumbering oak tree, and I tracked their course as they dipped their wings, while circling back to their familiar branch. I sensed comfort from them, warmth and forgiveness; my three lost birds who seemingly returned from that void between space and time

I had then meandered further down the lawn and read the names of other veterans who had gone before mine. I abruptly stopped when my eyes met his. His headstone immobilized me. I took in every bit of information. I rested my hands on his marker, and I buckled before it. I needed to let go, and I needed him to set me free.

I ran my hands over the smooth headstone and stood knowing the inscription was perfect, as he was perfect. I glanced at my brother and parent's plot, taking in one more look, and then to his. I studied the inscription, "Elio Lencioni."

I lingered for what seemed hours, and then I turned and walked away.

ACKNOWLEDGMENTS

Thank you to my two beautiful daughters for the gift of life, and boundless love.

To my dear friends Dave and Dori for their time, devotion, and endorsement.

To my amazing editor Stacey Smekofske of Edits by Stacey, extending her limitless expertise and guidance.

To the talented Tara Mayberry at TeaBerry Creative who produced my book covers.

And my sincerest gratitude to the infinite rows of solemn and inspirational remnants at Golden Gate National Cemetery.

Thank you

ABOUT THE AUTHOR

Tess Hamilton grew up in the San Francisco Bay Area. She attended writing workshops in San Francisco and Boise, Idaho, and has earned numerous five-star ratings for her first novel, *Thoughts of Leaving*. Tess has also received enthusiastic feedback from her readers.

The journey Tess began in *Thoughts of Leaving* continues in her latest novel, **Reappear**, as she soars ahead and continues to be inspired by her late father, who had always shared his magical imagination with her.

Tess currently surrounds herself in the vastness of Wyoming and blossoms from an internal transformation as she dives headfirst into the depths of her story, courageously pealing back layer-upon-layer of truths and exposing a voracious appetite, while sharing her enthusiasm with her readers.

Reappear is awakening and inspirational and will leave her audience yearning for more.

And more they will receive. Tess is currently composing her third book, which expands on many of the truths uncovered in her first two novels.

facebook.com/ThoughtsOfLeaving

Made in the USA
Las Vegas, NV
11 August 2021